Pilates and Calisthenics for Children

Using Imagery to Reinforce the Essential Principles of Movement

By Larkin Barnett, B.A., M.A. Dance

Editor: David Oriard
Book Design and Illustrations: Kristen Morales
Cover Design: Kristen Morales and Patti Jeffers

© 2010 Lorenz Educational Press, a Lorenz company, and its licensors. All rights reserved.
Printed in the United States of America

ISBN 978-1-4291-1714-2

BRIDGING
the Gaps in Education™
Lorenz Educational Press
P.O. Box 802 • Dayton, OH 45401-0802

For my father, Dr. Robert Barnett;
my mother, Suzanne Patricia Barnett;
and my grandparents, Dr. Edwin Barnett,
Agnes Barnett, Dr. William Kress McIntyre
and Mary Rose McIntyre

Thank you to my designer and illustrator,
Kristen Morales, and my editor, David Oriard.

Thank you to Dr. Eric W. Roberts,
PT, DPT, OCS, MTC for his contribution
concerning safety and precautions.

Thank you to Susan B. Dyer for her encouragement
to keep the book simple and fun.

Thank you to Stanley and Marilyn Katz.

Thank you to Glorianna Hunt Peale.

Table of Contents

*Chapters One, Two and Three Contain Your ABCs
— Alignment, Breathing and Core Control Basics*

Anytime, Anyplace Calisthenics Strength and Balance Program

Strength and Suppleness Pilates Mat Program

Anytime, Anyplace Standing Stretch Program

Foreword

Pilates and Calisthenics for Children is a wonderful resource for children, families, schools, and educators of all backgrounds and levels. Larkin Barnett's latest work is to be done, not merely read. As you peruse the contents of her book, you will find yourself engaging in the exercises because of her entertaining presentation and easy to follow directions. The Benefit Boxes at the end of the sections impart valuable information of how each exercise may benefit the children performing them. Her choice of visual images relate to both boys and girls while the fun titles will tempt the child to skip forward to read and perform the next exercise. The content of the material provided is valuable for building a strong foundation for a healthy lifestyle and is presented in a clean and organized manner, ensuring ease of use and a comprehensive understanding.

Ms. Barnett's use of creative visual imagery is the pathway to better body awareness and a deeper understanding of the body in motion. This innovative introduction of imagery with exercises for children helps to foster the use of all senses, enabling children to tap into their rich imagination while learning to integrate the mind body connection. It empowers children to become independent movers with proper body mechanics for exercise, which will become an ever-broadening cycle of learning throughout their lifetime. The focus on visualization helps children discover what few learn during their lives. The mind body connection is the key to a healthy body. A consistent profound inwardly directed focus on the images is the secret to this program's safety and success. It addresses the needs of the mind and body working together as a strong team.

This book is an inspirational resource for those who work with children and should be the cornerstone for all Physical Education programs in the United States. The knowledge bestowed upon its readers not only helps to prepare children for any sport, but also more importantly facilitates a strong foundation for healthier growth and development.

Aaron H. Spector, PT, DPT, OCS, MTC

Who is Joseph Pilates?

Joseph Pilates was born in 1880 in Germany. He suffered from asthma, rickets and rheumatic fever as a child. He became dedicated to exercise, strength training and sports to overcome his physical weakness. By the time he was 14 years old his physical self-improvement had been so successful that he modeled for anatomical charts.

In 1912, Pilates moved to England, where he taught self-defense to detectives. During World War I, he was taken prisoner of war because of his nationality. Pilates taught fellow captives his system of exercise. He began constructing equipment, removing bedsprings and attaching them to the bed frames so that patients could recover while still recumbent in a hospital bed. He is credited with saving the lives of many people during an influenza epidemic that struck England in 1918 because they practiced his breathing and exercise system.

Pilates returned to Germany after his release. His body-conditioning method made great headway in prominent dance circles. He referred to it as Contrology. He said the word meant "complete coordination of mind, body and spirit." Today it is referred to as The Pilates Method.

In 1926, Pilates embarked on a journey to the United States. Joseph met his wife, Clara, on the ship to New York. Together, they opened a fitness studio in a building they shared with the New York City Ballet. By the 1940s, Pilates had achieved great popularity in the dance world. By the 1960s, many dancers, athletes, actors and gymnasts were regular visitors to his studio.

Since the 1960s, the Pilates Method has grown to become one of the most popular fitness systems today.

Alignment

Chapter One

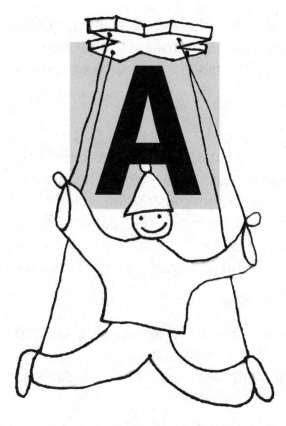

is for Alignment

Feel free to mix up the exercises in this book. You can even perform the calisthenics and Pilates Mat exercises within the same workout. Perform your Wall Stretches at the end of your workout when the muscles are warm. Be sure to include a power walking program or any cardio health activity to make your heart even healthier.

Let's Go Over the Basics

Anatomy-based visual imagery cues help to improve your posture. It is an ongoing process because your alignment is alive. It is important to use the cues to enhance your body awareness for the exercises. It is equally important to practice the imagery cues out in the real world.

When you put your bones in the right place you recruit the right muscles. A deeper understanding of alignment helps you move efficiently. You will have less wear and tear on your joints. Being off by one inch here or there can make all the difference in proper body mechanics.

Let's begin.

POSITION – STANDING ALIGNMENT

- Stand with your feet shoulder-width apart.

- Stack your hips, ribs, chest and head on top of each other like building blocks.

STEP ONE – YOUR EYE GAZE

- Paying attention to your eye gaze is the easiest way to align your head and spine.

- *Look up* and your back arches.

- *Look down* and your back rounds.

- *Look straight ahead* and your back is in the ideal neutral position.

You may choose to have someone demonstrate this for the class. Have the child stand sideways with his profile to the class. Ask him to *look up, look down and look straight ahead*, pausing in each position. You will immediately see the different back postures.

STEP TWO – YOUR HIP ALIGNMENT

- Picture the hips as a bowl full of popcorn. The rim of the bowl is your waistline. Place your hands on your waist.

- Tip your hips forward and dump popcorn on the floor in FRONT of you. This is called an anterior pelvic tilt. Your lower back arches.

- Tilt your hips backwards and dump popcorn on the floor BEHIND you. The lower back rounds into what is referred to as a posterior pelvic tilt.

- Place your hips in a balanced neutral position with a slight natural lower back arch. There aren't any pieces of popcorn falling out of the waistline. This is the ideal neutral pelvic postural position for the hips.

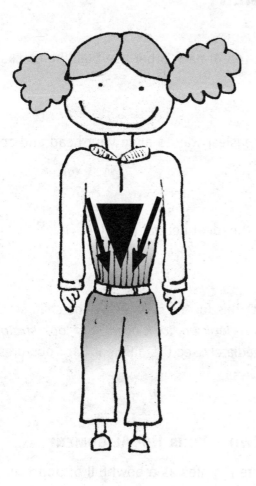

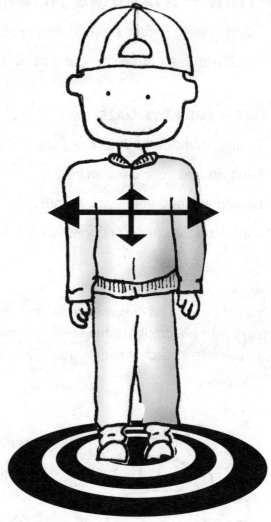

STEP THREE –
YOUR SHOULDER GIRDLE ALIGNMENT

- Use the image of tucking your shirt deep into the waistline of your pants.

- For example, visualize sliding your shoulder blades downward into your back trouser pockets.

- Picture your armpit area moving downward into your side trouser pockets.

- See your collarbone area sliding downward into the front waistband of your trousers.

STEP FOUR –
FIND YOUR BALANCE

- Keep your feet flat on the floor.

- Picture yourself standing in the center of a target located on the floor.

- Shift your entire body weight as a unit forward, backwards and sideways.

- Stop moving when you feel centered on the bull's eye of the target. Your weight will be evenly distributed over the balls, heels and outer/inward arches of your feet. You can check your balance by performing this on one leg.

Position – Sitting Alignment

Sit at your desk. Go over all of the identical standing alignment images you used previously. Focus on each alignment image one at a time – eye gaze, shoulder girdle, hips and feet. Say them aloud while the children "sit up and take notice" of their improved posture.

These alignment cues are a great posture activity for long car rides, the airplane, or while standing in a long line.

Pay Attention to Your Posture While Walking
Take a Walk Around the Room

- Stack your pelvis, ribs, chest and head on top of each other like building blocks.

- Imagine tucking your shirt into your pants to organize your shoulder girdle.

- Feel an imaginary belt drawing your abdominals in at the waist.

- Keep your pelvis level while walking as if your hips are full of popcorn. There won't be any popcorn pieces left behind you on the floor.

- Every time you take a step, picture walking in the center of imaginary targets. In fact, stop anytime and balance steadily on one leg on the bull's eye of the target. Practice standing in long lines at the grocery store, etc.

Benefits of Alignment

- Most of us have the poor habit of rounding our shoulders. Good posture makes more room for the lobes of the lungs. It allows you to take deeper breaths. This enhances the health of your respiratory system. Oxygen creates energy for our cells, even our brain cells.

- By improving our posture we have better concentration and more physical energy.

- We lift our shoulders unnecessarily to hold the telephone, a book or to use a computer keyboard. We overuse our shoulder shrug and neck muscles in everyday life. The alignment visual imagery cues will change incorrect, repeated movements of the upper body. This reduces tension and headaches.

- Alignment imagery cues help you to groove with gravity, instead of working against it. For example, when you habitually place all of your weight on one leg, leaning into one hip, many misalignments occur. You will experience less physical stress by balancing your body's weight evenly over both of your legs in the center of an imaginary target located on the floor.

Breathing
Chapter Two

**is for
Breathing**

There are two completely opposite kinds of breathing patterns to develop both flexibility and strength.

Balloon Breathing

Your breathing pattern for **stretching** is called deep relaxation **Balloon Breathing**. It helps you to simultaneously fill your body with air in three different directions. You will experience it in this chapter and incorporate it into your Wall Stretching Program. It is also excellent for your daily activities to calm your mind, relax or energize your body.

Pilates Lateral Breathing

The breathing pattern for **strengthening** is called **Lateral Breathing**. You will use this breathing pattern in your Pilates and Calisthenics Program. This breathing pattern strengthens your core. Your abdominal muscles must be ready to do the job of guiding EVERY Pilates and calisthenics movement. You will experience this form of Lateral Breathing for strength and endurance in chapters two and three. It will then be your aim to incorporate it into your Pilates Mat and Calisthenics Programs.

BALLOON BREATHING

YOUR INHALATIONS:

- It is an important image to visualize the air trickling in through a small, imaginary drinking straw. Otherwise you take in too much air too quickly. Visualize filling your entire trunk with air — like filling a balloon inside of you.

- You can practice this breathing in any position.

Preparation for Balloon Breathing

STEP ONE
Direct the air up and down, vertically along the spine. Feel TALL.

STEP TWO
Visualize directing your intake of air side to side, horizontally to expand your chest, belly and rib cage area. Feel WIDE.

STEP THREE
Picture your inhalations expanding your ribs and belly forward and back, sagittally. Feel THICK.

You are going to combine Steps One, Two and Three from above in a single inhalation. While practicing a single inhalation, say to yourself, "up and down, then side-to-side, and finally, forward and backward." Exhale. Try this several times.

START

- Take several long, slow, tranquil breaths to feel three-dimensional Balloon Breathing. Clearly picture each separate direction in your mind while inhaling. Visualize filling a balloon inside of your body with air. The balloon fills up and down, sideways, and forward and backward. Envision the balloon deflating while exhaling. Try this several times.

- Try this breathing technique several times with one hand on your belly and the other hand on your ribs. You will feel your hands move outward on the inhalations and move inward on the exhalations.

- Picture a basketball inside your body. The basketball fills on the inhalations. See your basketball expand to have length, width, and depth. It deflates on the exhalations. Practice this several times making your body feel TALL, WIDE and THICK.

- Breathe naturally without any strain or light-headedness. Never hold the breath. Practice for only 2 to 3 minutes a session. It takes time, patience and concentration.

- Look at the second hand on a clock. Find a comfortable, slow rhythm for you. This may be about 8 seconds on a clock for the inhalations and 8 seconds for the exhalations. Try to balance the length of your inhalations and exhalations.

- It may be more relaxing to breathe in through the nose and out through the mouth and nose. The nose filters impurities in the air.

- You can perform this Balloon Breathing technique in any position, while walking slowly and during your Wall Stretches.

- It is helpful for stress management anytime, anyplace.

- These are deep, slow and even breaths. Imagine your breathing is like the slow motion of a tranquil ocean wave.

Benefits of Deep Relaxation
Three-Dimensional Balloon Breathing

- Balloon Breathing is a practical exercise that can be practiced in any position anytime, anyplace. It reduces stress.

- Efficient breathing is directly related to calming the nervous system. The body is refreshed, which in turn calms the mind.

- Deep relaxation breathing is like an inner massage for the lungs.

- It improves your concentration, energy levels, digestion and sleep patterns.

- Use three-dimensional Balloon Breathing in your Wall Stretching Program to improve relaxation and range of motion.

LATERAL BREATHING

Joseph Pilates focused on proper breathing to strengthen the body. He advocated inhalations that filled the lungs and exhalations that emptied the lungs, to rid the body of toxins. The Pilates Method today refers to it as Lateral Breathing. Its chief purpose is to engage the deep core abdominals for EVERY Pilates' movement. This core control is equally important for EVERY calisthenics movement.

LATERAL BREATHING AGAINST A WALL

POSITION

- Stand with your back against a wall.

- Stand approximately one foot away from the wall.

- Place your legs together tightly with your thigh muscles engaged. Slightly bend your knees and squeeze your glutes.

- Feel the back of your head, upper back, back of your ribs and hips against the wall. Focus straight ahead with your chin level.

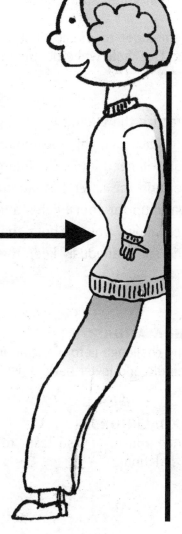

START

Your INHALATIONS:

- Place your hands flat on the sides of your ribs.

- Breathe in, allowing your ribs to push out laterally into your hands without expanding the belly. Don't take the air in too quickly or you won't be able to expand your rib cage from the inside out. You must picture directing the air into the back and sides of the ribs. You will feel the back of your ribs open and relax against the wall. This tactile feedback makes the wall a great place to practice your breathing.

Your EXHALATIONS:

- Actively exhale with a sound through pursed lips. Collapse the ribs as far as possible. Visualize the muscles of the ribs closing the ribs together in the front of the body like a corset. You will feel the two sides of your rib cage coming together in the front of your body.

- It is very helpful to draw your hands closer and closer together on the exhalations. This helps you feel the active engagement of the abdominals.

- You can even hug yourself tighter on the exhalations, drawing the forearms around you.

Repeat your Lateral Breathing 5-10 times per session.

Remember to direct air into the back of your rib cage keeping your abdominals muscles tight. Exhale while deepening your abdominal contraction.

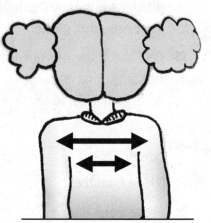

Practice the Lateral Breathing Against a Wall Exercise on a regular basis. This technique mimics the kind of breathing you will need for EVERY Pilates and calisthenics movement. Perform the Lateral Breathing Against the Wall Exercise to warm-up for your Pilates and Calisthenics Programs. Practice allows you to hold the abdominal muscles concave and simultaneously keep the upper body relaxed.

INHALATIONS:
The challenge is to direct air in along the back surfaces of your body – the shoulder blade area, middle and lower back — while keeping the abdominals tight in the front of the body.

EXHALATIONS:
Then you must also learn to deepen your abdominal contractions more and more on EACH exhalation.

Benefits of Pilates Lateral Breathing

■ This breathing technique can be practiced anytime, anyplace to provide inner support for your posture. Practice this practical internal exercise to make you feel more alert and alive.

■ It gives you more core abdominal control for the strength movements of Pilates and calisthenics.

■ It supports your spine in a proper neutral position.

■ Your breathing is the fuel necessary to help you find, feel and contract the elusive deep abdominal muscles.

■ The breathing also helps you blend one movement into the next.

■ It increases the inner core body temperature. It may help boost the immune system. This can enhance the body's resistance to colds and flu.

■ Your core becomes your "steering wheel" for all of your everyday movements. It provides stability and mobility for lifting heavy objects. It protects your joints and back.

■ Core control can give you that extra edge to soar past competitors in sports. It improves stamina, speed and motor control.

■ Moving from your core within gym workouts with weights or cardio equipment is extremely important. It can prevent overuse syndromes, injury and burn out.

Lateral Breathing must be the main focus of EVERY Pilates and calisthenics movement. Practice it against the wall right before your workouts for the proper tactile feedback. Remember whether you are taking air in or letting it out, the abdominals NEVER Relax.

Before you perform any of the exercises be sure you are ready to move. This is like an airline pilot who checks his instruments before he moves the airplane. For example, isometrically contract your abdominals while exhaling, relax your shoulders, squeeze your glutes – and then move.

Control

Chapter Three

is for Control

The Core Control Champion Exercise

Your center abdominal area is the most important ingredient for Pilates and your calisthenics exercises. It is the area between your lower ribs and hips. The abdominals form THE FOUNDATION of your body's powerful midsection.

The abdominal muscles are made up of four layers of powerful elastic bands. These muscle fibers crisscross to form an anatomical girdle. They lie across each other at various angles. The abdominals work together as a unit to produce movement. Nevertheless, the Core Control Champion Exercise uses visual imagery to isolate the different layers with the goal of finding and feeling them contract more.

Having a mental picture of your abdominal muscles is the key to toned strong stomach muscles. The Core Control Champion Exercise helps you master deep core strength through visual imagery.

Notice how each core control visual image throughout the book has movement built into it. For example, contract your abdominals like a corset cinching together.

THE CORE CONTROL CHAMPION EXERCISE
+ LATERAL BREATHING
_____
= DEEP CORE ABDOMINAL STRENGTH

When you practice your Lateral Breathing with the Core Control Champion Exercise, you acquire deep abdominal strength. You will learn to never let your abdominals relax. In fact, use the following five steps and five images to help you keep inwardly shaping the abdominal muscles.

1 Dragon Mouth Clamping Shut

2 Cinch in your ribs like malleable armor

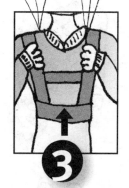

3 Scoop your abs back and up like a parachute harness

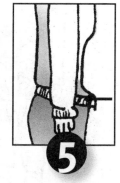

4 Wrap your abs in vines

5 Sink your navel to your spine

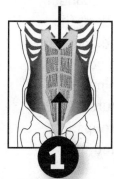

1 Outermost abs: Rectus Abdominis

2 Second layer of abs: External Obliques

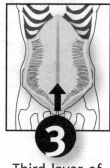

3 Third layer of abs: Internal Obliques

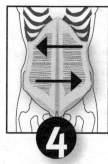

4 Fourth and deepest layer of abs: Transversus Abdominis

5 Fifth layer beneath the abs: Hip Flexors

CORE CONTROL CHAMPION
+ LATERAL BREATHING AGAINST A WALL EXERCISE

POSITION

- Stand with your back against a wall.
- Stand approximately one foot away from the wall.
- Place your legs together tightly with your thigh muscles engaged. Slightly bend your knees and squeeze your glutes.
- Feel the back of your head, upper back, back of your ribs and hips against the wall. Focus straight ahead with your chin level.

START

STEP ONE

- Inhale directing your air into the back of your rib cage only. Exhale while picturing your abdominals as a Dragon Mouth Clamping Shut along the front of your trunk.

STEP TWO

- Inhale while keeping your abdominals tight. Exhale. Picture your abdominals as Malleable Armor cinching your ribs together in front.

STEP THREE

- Inhale, picturing the air expanding the back of the rib cage. Exhale. Picture your abdominals as a Parachute Harness that scoops in, back and up.

STEP FOUR

- Inhale, maintaining your deep abdominal contraction. Exhale. Picture your abdominals as Strong Vines wrapping around your trunk.

STEP FIVE

- Inhale into the back surfaces of the body. Exhale. Sink your navel to your spine.

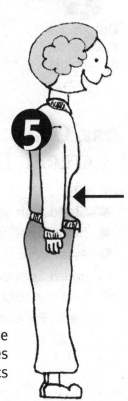

Repeat the Five Steps 3 – 5 times. This Core Control Champion Exercise can be practiced in any position anytime, anyplace. Practice makes perfect. It is a fun challenge to add it to your Pilates and calisthenics exercises.

Benefits of Core Control

■ The Core Control Champion Exercise is a practical exercise that can be used anytime, anyplace, while in any position.

■ A strong core offers limitless reserves of power for any activity or heavy lifting.

■ Moving from your core promotes ease and efficiency of movement.

■ Initiating movements from the core instead of your limbs (arms and legs) helps you to develop physical balance and strength.

■ Mastering this centering technique provides safety and success for Pilates, calisthenics, sports, dance, martial arts, gym workouts and everyday life.

■ Persistent practice of The Core Control Champion Exercise becomes a mental trigger to activate your center and breathing for your Pilates and Calisthenics Programs. It is a good warm-up exercise.

■ The Core Control Champion Exercise provides an internal massage for the organs, which lie beneath the abdominal wall.

Calisthenic Exercises

Chapter Four

These are practical exercises you can do anyplace, anytime...and they don't require any equipment. Calisthenics just require you and your body's weight working in harmony with gravity. You will do all of the calisthenics Pilates-style by using anatomy-based visual imagery that encapsulates essential principles of movement. You will learn to add elements of posture, spinal alignment, dynamic breathing, as well as abdominal power. The point is to fine-tune the movements you know. Through practice you find that precision and attention to the details makes the movements challenging and safe.

JOYFUL JUMPING JACKS!

Jumping Jacks can be done anywhere. Traditional Jumping Jacks are performed in the U.S. military. They are an easy anytime, anyplace cardio exercise. They focus on conditioning and total body endurance.

IMAGINE ...
A Visual Imagery Guide

Use your ABC Guide Boxes for EVERY repetition of each exercise. These Boxes are located throughout the book. They contain visual imagery that encapsulates the essential principles of movement. These Alignment, Breathing and Core Control images ensure proper total body mechanics. Say your ABC images out loud while you train. And you really can't say and practice these ABCs enough. For example, "Tighten the stomach muscles like strong vines that wrap around the body." Become your own coach. Watch the body completely transform before your eyes on each repetition because the ABCs provide the secret to perfect form! Alignment, Breathing and Core Control visual imagery utilizes your mind/body connection for safety and success.

TEACHING TIPS

Avoid if you have any leg or back problems.

- Perform Jumping Jacks for a number of repetitions or a time period. You may want to perform several sets of Jumping Jacks. Walk in place between sets in order to build up your endurance. In fact, warm-up with 5-10 minutes of vigorous walking in place or even marching.

- Jump like an Olympic athlete by focusing on the quality of your movements, not the quantity of your repetitions.

- Use your visual images in the ABC Guide Boxes to help you pay attention to proper form. Your focus stays on these Alignment, Breathing and Core Control visual images.

POSITION

- Start in an upright standing position with the feet together and hands to the side.

START

- Begin the movement by jumping vertically while at the same time move the feet out shoulder-width apart and the hands above the head.

- Return to starting position and repeat for a number of repetitions or a time period.

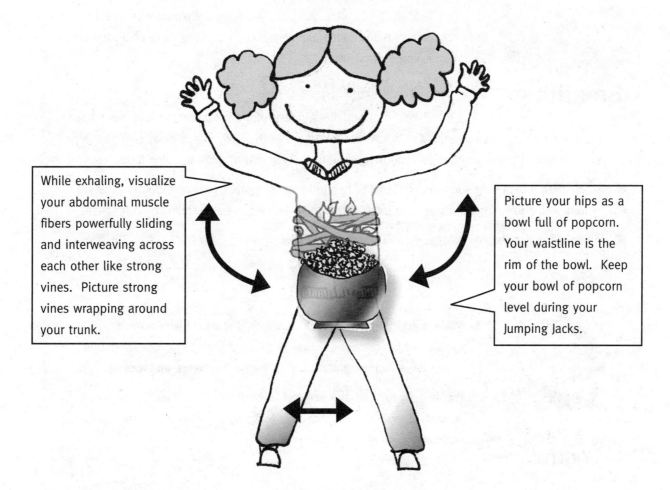

While exhaling, visualize your abdominal muscle fibers powerfully sliding and interweaving across each other like strong vines. Picture strong vines wrapping around your trunk.

Picture your hips as a bowl full of popcorn. Your waistline is the rim of the bowl. Keep your bowl of popcorn level during your Jumping Jacks.

A

is for
Alignment

Jump without gripping and tensing the upper body muscles. Keep your shoulders down away from your ears.

■ Imagine you have big balloons next to your ears each time you lift your arms overhead.

■ Feel your arms float up but your shoulder blade area relaxes downward toward your back trouser pockets. The shoulder blade area is located along the upper back. Eventually you breathe out on every two jumping jacks.

This image reinforces the feeling of sequential movements with a balanced upper body musculature and freedom of motion.

■ Land softly on the ground with your feet planted right in the center of an imaginary target located on the ground.

■ Picture your hips as a bowl full of popcorn. Your waistline is the rim of the bowl. Keep your bowl of popcorn level during your Jumping Jacks. There are no pieces of popcorn falling on the floor in front or in back of the body! **See figure on Page 21.**

B

is for
Breathing

Paying attention to your breathing is the key to better endurance for fitness, sports, dance, yoga, Pilates and martial arts – and for life. It also provides the "fuel" for tightening your stomach muscles. Always move by engaging your core abdominal muscles. Arms and legs do not lead the movement. Keep the focus on the contraction of your stomach muscles during Jumping Jacks. Move the body, as a total unit, not isolated segments.

■ Inhale to prepare.

■ Exhale out loud like a powerful dragon when the feet move apart and the hands move overhead. The exhalation occurs when the body jumps away from the floor to resist gravity's downward pull. You breathe out on every two or more Jumping Jacks.

■ Exhale with a breathing sound to remind you to continuously tighten your core abdominals in toward your spine. This protects your back. Your body remains in perfect dynamic alignment.

■ Inhale when the feet come together and squeeze your glutes.

C

is for
Control

■ While exhaling, visualize your abdominal muscle fibers powerfully sliding and interweaving across each other like strong vines. Picture strong vines wrapping around your trunk. **See figure on Page 21.**

This helps you "fire" the deepest layer of your abdominal muscles. It provides deep muscular stability. Make sure the core stays tight and the movements are quick and controlled.

POWER PUSH-UPS!

IMAGINE ...
A Visual Imagery Guide

The images are teaching cues to help you prepare, initiate and execute each movement properly – from point A to point B. Stabilize first, then move. For example, slide your shoulder girdle downward, navel back, front ribs in and down, glutes squeezed, upper thighs glued together and focus on your breathing. This all happens at once BEFORE you move and during EVERY repetition of a Push-up!

Push-ups can be done anywhere. They are the oldest and most common exercises used by the military and competitive sports teams around the world to gauge overall fitness. They utilize functional training by involving the body as a total unit.

You may chose to start by doing a Wall Push-up or a Bent-knee Push-up (knees on the floor). Perform Bent-knee Push-ups by supporting the lower body on the knees instead of the toes. Over time the muscles of the arms and upper trunk build up strength to the point where they can support the motion with perfect form. As you get stronger, extend one leg backward into the traditional Full Push-up position. Gradually progress to the traditional Full Push-up with both legs straight.

TEACHING TIPS

Avoid if you have any back, shoulder or knee problems.
Be careful if you have any neck issues.

- Perform 1-3 sets of 10-15 repetitions.

- You may want to gradually build up your strength over time. It is more important that you pay attention to proper form rather than the number of repetitions. Use your visual images located in the ABC Guide Boxes.

- You may want to use a slightly cushioned mat, thick towel, blanket or carpet.

WALL PUSH-UPS

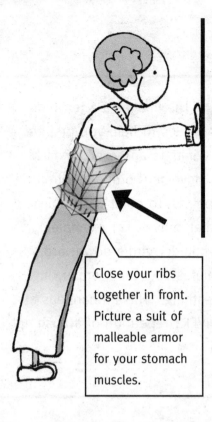

Close your ribs together in front. Picture a suit of malleable armor for your stomach muscles.

POSITION

■ Stand a few feet away from a wall.

■ Place your hands on the wall in front of you. The hands are a few inches below shoulder level. This keeps the shoulders from hiking upward toward your ears. You may choose to place the hands closer together to work the tricep muscles located along the back of your upper arms. Place the hands farther apart to emphasize the chest.

START

■ Stand a few feet away from a wall and push away from the wall with the arms. Keep your chin toward your chest slightly.

BENT-KNEE PUSH-UPS

POSITION

■ Kneel on all fours. Support your body weight on your hands and legs.

■ Hands are directly under your shoulders and knees are under your hips. The legs are together.

■ Keep your head in line with your spine, and look down at the floor. Do not drop your head.

START

■ Raise and lower the body using the arms. The Bent-knee Push-up should be deep, the chest near the floor.

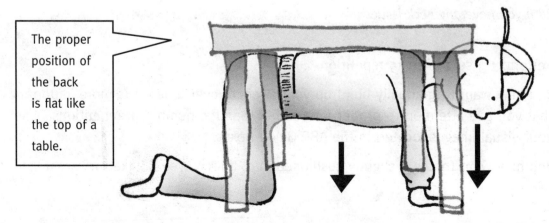

The proper position of the back is flat like the top of a table.

FULL PUSH-UPS

POSITION

- Begin on all fours. Hands are directly under your shoulders. Straighten the legs behind you. The legs are close together.

- Keep your head in line with your spine and look down at the floor.

START

- Raise and lower the body in one piece. The Full Push-up should be deep, the chest near the floor.

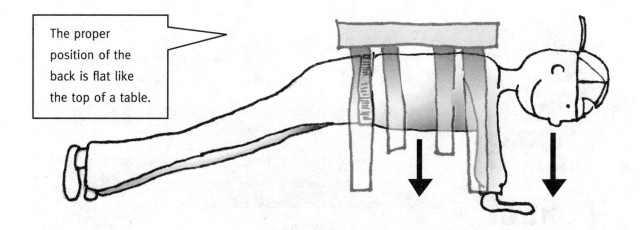

The proper position of the back is flat like the top of a table.

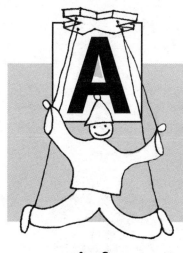

is for
Alignment

- Feel your entire shoulder girdle area slide downward toward your waistline. This is like tucking your shirt into your trousers — and then tighten your imaginary belt around your waistline.

- Keep your hips level even in the plank Full Push-up position. The hips stay in line with the spine.

is for
Breathing

■ Inhale to prepare. Exhale powerfully each time you move the body away from the floor (or away from the wall during Wall Push-ups). Exhale with a powerful breathing sound to remind you to tighten your stomach muscles.

is for
Control

Focus on the Push-up working the body's core! You don't want your ribs to relax toward the floor or have a sway back like a horse. The proper position of the back is flat like the top of a table. **See figures on Pages 24 and 25.**

■ Close your ribs together in front. Picture a suit of malleable armor for your stomach muscles.

■ Exhale powerfully, while feeling the armor forcefully pulled together, inward and downward along the front of your body. Cinch your armor around your rib cage and then move it into your hips.

Super Sit-ups!

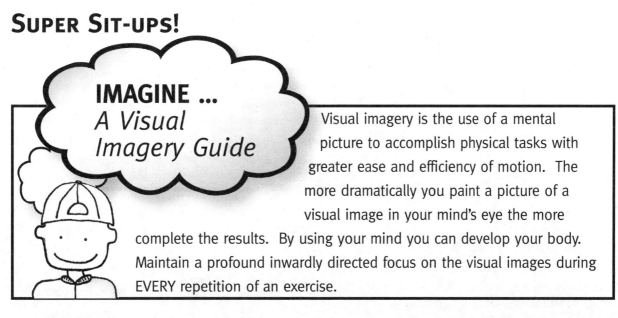

IMAGINE ...
A Visual Imagery Guide

Visual imagery is the use of a mental picture to accomplish physical tasks with greater ease and efficiency of motion. The more dramatically you paint a picture of a visual image in your mind's eye the more complete the results. By using your mind you can develop your body. Maintain a profound inwardly directed focus on the visual images during EVERY repetition of an exercise.

Sit-ups can be done anywhere. They are the most common exercise for the abdominal muscles. You will be doing a Curl-up. It is safer than a full Sit-up where the lower back leaves the floor. The half Curl-up eliminates the involvement of the hip flexors, and makes it an effective isolation exercise for the abdominals.

Teaching Tips

Avoid if you have any abdominal or back problems.
Support your head and neck with your hands without placing your chin on your chest.

- Perform 1-3 sets of 10-15 repetitions.

- Pay attention to perfect form on every repetition. Your visual imagery ABC Guide Boxes will help you have proper body mechanics.

- You may want to use a slightly cushioned mat, thick towel, blanket or carpet.

Position

- Lie on the mat, on your back, knees bent, and feet flat. Your heels will be about 12 inches away from your hips. Your legs are pressed together tightly.

- The hands* are placed behind the neck.

*The hands only form a shelf to support the weight of the head, so that the neck muscles can relax during the movement. This keeps you from curling up from the hands, and arms. Instead use the abdominal contraction to initiate and follow through from point A and return to point B.

Start

- Inhale to prepare.

- Exhale each time you curl up.

- Curl the shoulders towards the pelvis. The upper back leaves the floor. The lower back should not leave the floor. Return.

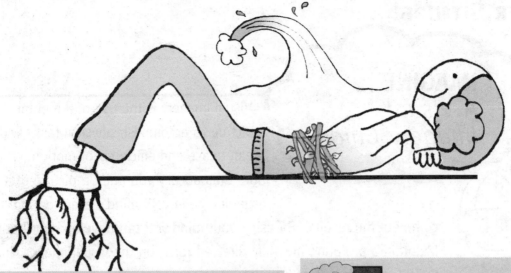

Picture your shoulder girdle area as a shirt that you tuck into the waistline of your pants. Slide your shoulder girdle toward your feet as you curl up and down. Keep an imaginary orange between your chin and chest

is for
Alignment

This imagery will help keep your shoulders relaxed and away from your ears. When you organize your shoulder girdle, it is easier to feel your deep abdominals contract inward toward your spine. Avoid pushing the abdominals outward.

Feel your feet sink like roots into the floor. **See figure above.** Visualize your feet on the middle of a compass. Ground and stretch your feet out to the north, south, east, and west directions of your compass.

is for
Breathing

Picture your body continuously curling over a huge ocean wave while moving up and down. **See figure above.**

Use the power of your exhalations to access your deepest abdominals when curling up.

Inhale to return your upper body to the floor.

Whether you are breathing in or out, continuously contract your abdominals. Yes, even each time you return to the floor! The title of the Abdominal Song is, "Once You Find Them, Never Let Them Go!"

is for
Control

Experiment with the following image to help you feel your abdominals contract and stabilize your back. For example, for the contraction of your stomach muscles, picture wrapping your stomach muscles together tighter and tighter like a strong vine during each repetition. **See figure above.**

Imagine there are several tennis balls in between your legs – from your ankles to your knees and inner thighs. Squeeze your glutes and leg muscles firmly together against the tennis balls.

Cough to find these important hip, base of the hip, and upper thigh muscles. Feeling them helps you stabilize and find your deep stomach muscles.

STRONG SQUATS

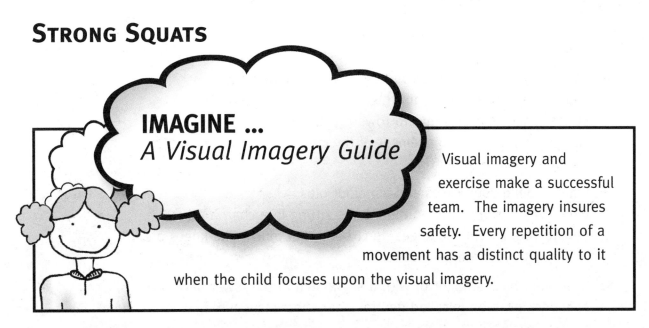

IMAGINE ...
A Visual Imagery Guide

Visual imagery and exercise make a successful team. The imagery insures safety. Every repetition of a movement has a distinct quality to it when the child focuses upon the visual imagery.

Squats can be done anywhere. Perform a Squat by bending at the knees and hips. The torso lowers and then reversing direction stand upright. From point A to point B, the deep core abdominal muscles contract to support the back. This also helps to lift the weight of your body upward out of the legs. The torso leans forward to maintain balance with the spine and head in one long line. This is as if you are going to sit in a chair, a little ways behind you. It is important to keep the back straight even though the torso leans. The chest stays lifted and the eye gaze never drops downward.

The Squat is primarily a lower body exercise. It is often called the "king of exercises." Many believe it produces more and faster muscle growth than any other exercise.

TEACHING TIPS

Avoid if you have any leg or back problems.
Stay with a range of motion that is comfortable for you.

- Perform 1-3 sets of 10-15 repetitions. Perfect form is always more important than the number of repetitions.

- The important teaching cues for proper form are contained in the visual imagery ABC Guide Boxes.

POSITION

- Stand with your feet shoulder width apart and the knees slightly bent.

- Point your toes straight ahead.

- Your arms are hanging straight at your sides.

- Keep your head straight and looking forward throughout the exercise.

START
Step One

- Contract your core before you begin. For example, squeeze your glutes and engage your thigh muscles. Contract your stomach muscles inward toward your spine. Maintain the engagement of the core throughout every repetition.

- Inhale. Bend your knees and aim your hips back. This movement is a little bit like sitting in a chair a ways behind you. Except the knees don't bend that much. The knees are in line with your ankles, not toes.

- Keep your back straight or with a slight arch in the lower back. This back position is called neutral. Your chest stays lifted.

- On the descent you can raise your arms out in front of you. This acts as a counter balance. It controls the movement. You don't feel like you are falling backward.

Step Two

- Exhale powerfully. Give your glutes an extra squeeze to help you on your way back up to standing. The arms return to your sides.

**is for
Alignment**

- Imagine your feet are securely planted in the center of a compass during your Squats. Distribute the weight of your body evenly between the balls of your feet and your heels – to the north, south, east and west directions of the compass. **See figure above.**

- During the first part of the Squat imagine you are sitting in a chair. Hover just above the chair before returning to standing.

- Inhale as you bend your knees.

- Exhale with a long, powerful breath sound as you straighten your legs. You may want to purse your lips. This makes your breathing more dynamic.

**is for
Breathing**

**is for
Control**

- Imagine your glutes are fastened together by a strong zipper.

- Your abdominal muscles are constantly contracting. This feels like malleable armor. The armor wraps around the entire trunk. Focus on this image to feel your abdominal muscles carve inward and upward. **See figure above.**

LIVELY LUNGES

Lunges can be done anywhere. The Lunge is another weight training exercise. It involves your body weight moving away from gravity's downward pull. It strengthens the core, legs and glutes.

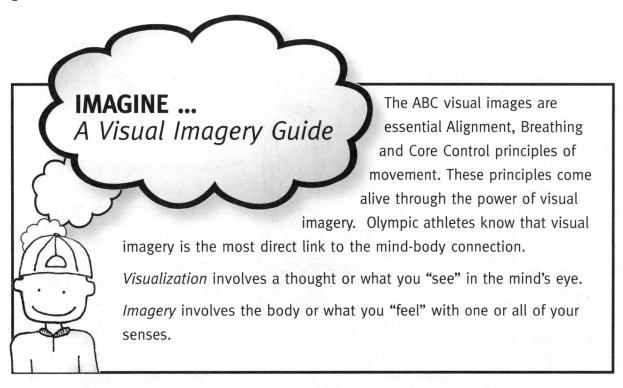

IMAGINE ...
A Visual Imagery Guide

The ABC visual images are essential Alignment, Breathing and Core Control principles of movement. These principles come alive through the power of visual imagery. Olympic athletes know that visual imagery is the most direct link to the mind-body connection.

Visualization involves a thought or what you "see" in the mind's eye.

Imagery involves the body or what you "feel" with one or all of your senses.

TEACHING TIPS

Avoid if you have any leg or back problems.
Keep the range of motion comfortable for you.

- ■ Perform 1-3 sets of 10-15 repetitions for each leg.

- ■ EVERY repetition must involve a profound inwardly directed focus. Make sure to maintain the alignment and posture throughout the movement. Focus on constantly deepening your abdominal contraction. Squeeze the glutes every time you return from a lunge.

- ■ A small step forward uses primarily the thigh muscles. A larger step uses mainly the glutes.

- ■ Encourage the children to say the visual imagery teaching cues out loud. These are located in the ABC Guide Boxes. Help them to become their own coach for a life-time of fitness safety and success.

POSITION

- ■ Stand with the feet shoulder-width apart. Your knees are slightly bent and the toes are pointed straight ahead.

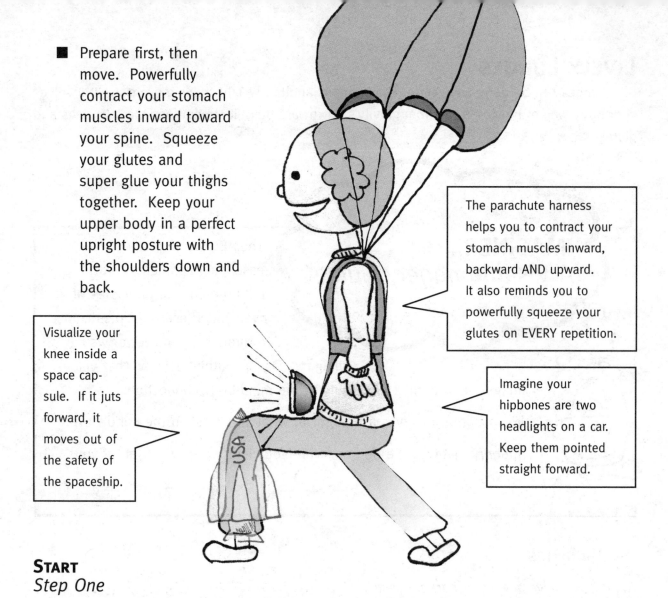

■ Prepare first, then move. Powerfully contract your stomach muscles inward toward your spine. Squeeze your glutes and super glue your thighs together. Keep your upper body in a perfect upright posture with the shoulders down and back.

The parachute harness helps you to contract your stomach muscles inward, backward AND upward. It also reminds you to powerfully squeeze your glutes on EVERY repetition.

Visualize your knee inside a space capsule. If it juts forward, it moves out of the safety of the spaceship.

Imagine your hipbones are two headlights on a car. Keep them pointed straight forward.

START
Step One

■ Inhale to prepare. Take a step forward while exhaling. Land with the heel first and roll gently through the foot. Bend at the knees, making sure you descend with slow controlled momentum. Your hips lower.

■ The front knee should be at a 90-degree angle and directly above the ankle, not forward over the toes.

■ Your back remains straight in a neutral position. Your eye gaze does not drop down. Look straight ahead, keeping your chin level.

Step Two

■ Inhale to prepare. Exhale to engage your stomach and glute muscles. Return to the starting position during this long, powerful exhalation. Drive upward from the front leg. Change legs.

Congratulations – you've completed one repetition. Alternate your legs each time.

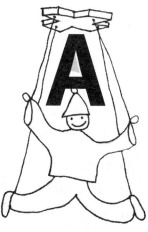

is for
Alignment

- Picture your shoulder girdle area as a shirt that you tuck deep into the waistline of your pants. Then close an imaginary belt tightly around the waistline of your pants.

- The hips don't twist. Imagine your hipbones are two headlights on a car. Keep them pointed straight forward.

- Your knee is directly in line with your ankle, not jutting forward over your toes. Visualize your knee inside a space capsule. If it juts forward, it moves out of the safety of the spaceship. **See figure on Page 32.**

is for
Breathing

- Inhale to prepare for Step One AND Step Two of each Lunge. Exhale each time you are moving. Exhale through pursed lips to help you contract the deep muscles of the abdominals, glutes and legs. Keep coaching yourself to deepen the abdominals more and more. Your breath is the fuel for finding the deep core abdominals.

is for
Control

- Whether you are stepping forward into the Lunge or returning to standing, keep inwardly shaping your abdominals. See yourself wearing a parachute harness. It is attached to a parachute above you. The parachute harness helps you to contract your stomach muscles inward, backward AND upward. **See figure on Page 32.** It also reminds you to powerfully squeeze your glutes on EVERY repetition. The parachute image keeps the weight of your body up and out of the legs. Defy gravity. Hover and control your landings from the core.

Sit on the Wall

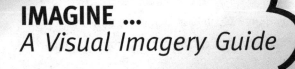

IMAGINE ...
A Visual Imagery Guide

Visual imagery results in an ever-broadening cycle of learning about experiential anatomy and how the body functions. A deep understanding of the human body in efficient motion will influence children's participation in sports, dance, martial arts and recreational activities.

The Sit on the Wall exercise can be done anywhere. The wall is a tool to make us aware of our postural habits and to improve them. You will look like you're sitting on an invisible chair. Sitting on a phantom chair is a great core and leg strengthener. It improves your posture.

Teaching Tips

Avoid if you have any leg or back problems.

- ■ You will need a wall.

- ■ Perform this exercise 2-3 times with perfect form.

- ■ Your ABC Guide Boxes contain visual imagery teaching cues to sculpt a stronger and more aligned body.

Position

- ■ Stand against the wall. Your feet are one large step away from the wall. This ensures that when you bend the knees they will be in line with the ankles, not the toes.

- ■ Your legs are in parallel with the hips, knees, and feet pointing straight ahead.

- ■ The neck lengthens slightly when you gently place the base of the head against the wall. The eye gaze is directly forward with the chin level.

- ■ Open the chest and upper back. Press the shoulders back toward the wall.

- ■ The ribs do not protrude in the front of the body. You must engage the abdominal muscles in order to close and relax the ribs along the front of the body.

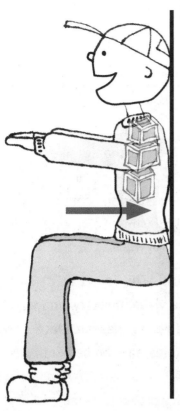

START
Step One

- Bend the knees. Raise your arms in front of you. Keep them slightly below shoulder level. The arms reach to the opposite side of the room. They will be parallel with the legs.

- Lower down until the hips and knees are at 90-degree angles. You should look like you are seated in a chair. Hold the position for a few seconds. But it is more important to keep the head, upper back and hips in contact with the wall. Your back is in neutral position. Avoid tucking your pelvis underneath you. The entire length of the spine remains against the wall as you slide down and up.

Step Two

- Pull your abdominals in and up and slide back up to standing. Keep your hips in contact with the wall. Allow your arms to return to your sides.

Keep your movements slow and controlled. Repeat 2-3 times.

**is for
Alignment**

- The pelvis, chest, head and ribs remain stacked on top of each other like building blocks. **See figure above.**

**is for
Breathing**

- Continue breathing when you perform Sit on the Wall.

- Direct your inhalations along the entire back surfaces of your body – the shoulder blade area, middle, and lower back.

- Use your powerful exhalations to simultaneously engage your abdominals, glutes, pelvic floor and leg muscles.

**is for
Control**

- Wrap your arms tightly across the front of your rib cage. Each time you exhale use your hands and arms to draw the muscles of the ribs together. This tactile hugging motion helps to contract the abdominals. You will feel the back of your ribs sink into the wall like molasses.

- Picture your navel sinking in toward your spine. **See figure above.**

Sit-ups with a Twist

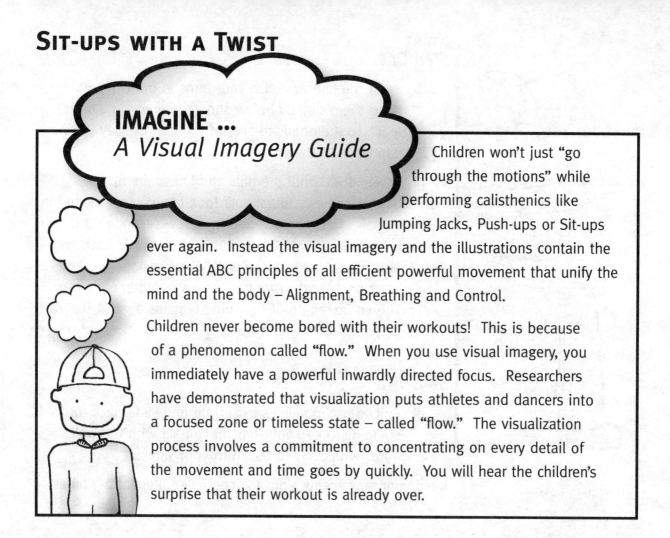

IMAGINE ...
A Visual Imagery Guide

Children won't just "go through the motions" while performing calisthenics like Jumping Jacks, Push-ups or Sit-ups ever again. Instead the visual imagery and the illustrations contain the essential ABC principles of all efficient powerful movement that unify the mind and the body – Alignment, Breathing and Control.

Children never become bored with their workouts! This is because of a phenomenon called "flow." When you use visual imagery, you immediately have a powerful inwardly directed focus. Researchers have demonstrated that visualization puts athletes and dancers into a focused zone or timeless state – called "flow." The visualization process involves a commitment to concentrating on every detail of the movement and time goes by quickly. You will hear the children's surprise that their workout is already over.

The Sit-up with a Twist exercise can be done anywhere. It primarily targets the oblique abdominals that crisscross along the front of the body.

Teaching Tips

Avoid if you have any abdominal, back or neck problems.

- Perform 1-3 sets of 15 repetitions on each side.

- Use the visual imagery cues to really focus on keeping your midsection contracted throughout the entire exercise. These are located in your ABC Guide Boxes.

- The aim is to twist the torso toward your knee. Don't just move your arm.

- Move up and down slowly without momentum. The most important tip is to NEVER relax the abdominal muscles on the way down toward the floor. This way you'll be able to deepen...deepen...deepen your stomach muscles more on EVERY repetition.

- You may want to use a cushioned mat, towel, blanket or carpet.

POSITION

■ Lie down on your back.

■ Bend your right leg with the foot flat on the floor.

■ Bend your left leg and place your ankle on your right thigh.

■ Overlap your hands and place them at the base of your head. The elbows stay wide and open throughout the movement.

Picture a big X along the front of your trunk. Every time you lift up, feel the X shrink into the center point.

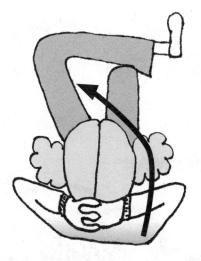

START

■ Inhale to prepare. Exhale powerfully to contract the abdominal muscles. Twist slightly at the waist. Raise your right shoulder and cross it toward your left knee.

■ Slowly lower your shoulder back to the starting position.

After completing 15 repetitions change to the other side.

is for
Alignment

■ Relax your shoulder girdle area down away from your head. This feels like you are tucking a shirt deep into the waistline of a pair of trousers. Tightly close an imaginary belt around the waistline of the pants to feel your abdominals contract.

■ Twist your torso like a seat belt crossing your body. This rotational movement helps you feel the squeeze in your oblique abdominal muscles on the side that you're working.

- Whether you are exhaling to move up or inhaling to move down, keep inwardly shaping your stomach muscles. They never pooch out. Exhale forcefully to scoop them in toward your spine instead.

is for Breathing

- Picture a big X along the front of your trunk. Feel the X shrink into the center point. **See figure on Page 37.** This deep abdominal sensation happens EVERY time the body lifts up.

is for Control

SUPERMAN

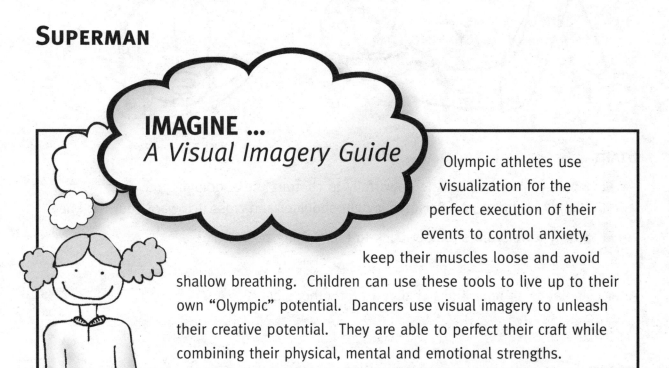

IMAGINE ...
A Visual Imagery Guide

Olympic athletes use visualization for the perfect execution of their events to control anxiety, keep their muscles loose and avoid shallow breathing. Children can use these tools to live up to their own "Olympic" potential. Dancers use visual imagery to unleash their creative potential. They are able to perfect their craft while combining their physical, mental and emotional strengths.

The Superman exercise can be done anywhere. It strengthens your core.

TEACHING TIPS

Avoid if you have any back, neck or hip problems.

- Repeat this exercise 3-5 times. Hold for 3 seconds.
- This exercise makes improvements in your posture. Pay strict attention to the teaching cues located in the ABC Guide Boxes.
- You may want to use a mat, towel, blanket or carpet.

Feel as if you are flying like Superman. Look down at the tops of the buildings.

POSITION

■ Lie face down on the floor. Your arms and legs are extended. Your arms are overhead with the palms facing each other. Your legs are externally rotated in the hip joint.

START

■ Inhale to prepare. Exhale and contract your abdominals away from the floor BEFORE you move. Sink your navel in toward your spine. Close your ribs together in the front of the body. Visualize a corset cinching together tightly.

■ Exhale again. Lift your arms and legs off the floor as if you were Superman flying. Squeeze your glutes and abdominals. Gently lengthen your legs to the wall behind you.

■ Keep your shoulders down away from your ears.

■ Keep your head/neck in a neutral position. This is accomplished by keeping your eye gaze down.

■ Hold for three seconds. Keep your breathing steady and even.

■ Slowly lower your arms and legs back to the starting position. Don't relax your core as you lightly touch the floor; repeat.

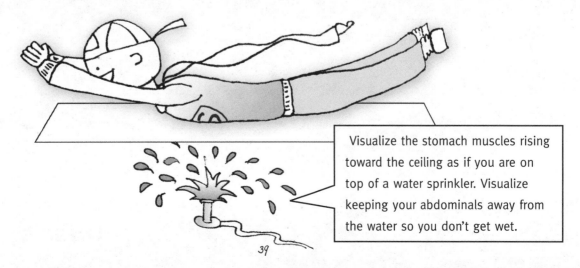

Visualize the stomach muscles rising toward the ceiling as if you are on top of a water sprinkler. Visualize keeping your abdominals away from the water so you don't get wet.

You may also choose to lift the opposite arm and leg instead of both arms and legs.

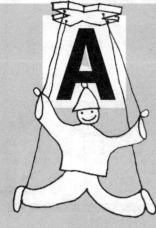

is for
Alignment

- Feel as if you are flying like Superman. Look down at the tops of the buildings. **See figure on Page 39.** Your downcast eye gaze keeps your head/neck in alignment with the rest of the spine. The back of your neck stays long. Your head weighs approximately 11 pounds and should never drop. It always remains supported and part of the spine.

- Your shoulder girdle area slides downward toward your hips. This feels like Superman's cape when he is flying. The cape is being drawn downward along his back because he is speeding through the air. This image keeps the shoulders, shoulder blades, armpits and collarbone area from hiking up toward the ears.

is for
Breathing

- Pay attention to your exhalations. Blow out with the strength of Superman to help you contract your core.

is for
Control

- Feel a large, strong zipper along your glutes. Zipper the gluteal muscles together to access the thigh muscles and support the back.

- Continuously contract your abdominals to hover like Superman. Keep them inwardly shaping away from the floor. Visualize the stomach muscles rising toward the ceiling as if you are on top of a water sprinkler. **See figure on Page 39.**

DONKEY KICKS

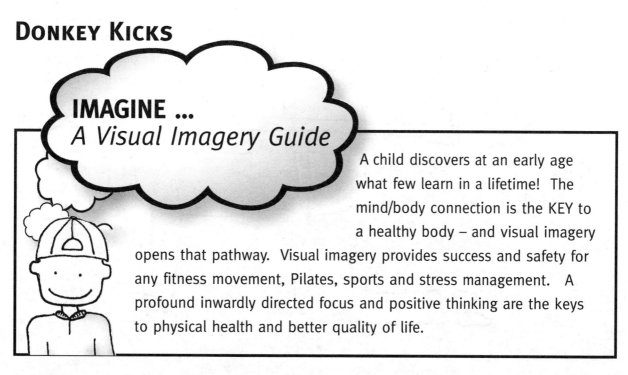

IMAGINE ...
A Visual Imagery Guide

A child discovers at an early age what few learn in a lifetime! The mind/body connection is the KEY to a healthy body – and visual imagery opens that pathway. Visual imagery provides success and safety for any fitness movement, Pilates, sports and stress management. A profound inwardly directed focus and positive thinking are the keys to physical health and better quality of life.

The Donkey Kick exercise can be done anywhere. This is an excellent core, glute and leg strengthener.

TEACHING TIPS

Avoid if you have any back or leg problems.
Visualize your head as a lollipop on a stick. Be sure your eye gaze remains down.

- Perform 1-3 sets of 15 repetitions for each leg. The number of repetitions depends on your ability to maintain perfect form.

- Your ABC Guide Boxes contain the images for safety and success.

- You may choose to use a cushioned mat, towel, blanket or carpet. A towel can be folded and placed under your knees.

POSITION

- Kneel on all fours.

- The hands are placed underneath the shoulder joints.

- The knees are lined up with the hip joints.

- The back is in neutral position supported by the abdominals.

- The elbows are straight but not locked.

- The head is level because the eyes are focused directly in between the hands.

START
Step One

- Inhale. Exhale as you curl your back into spine flexion. This looks like a Halloween cat arching its back. Your back looks like the letter C. Bring your right knee and left elbow toward your chest.

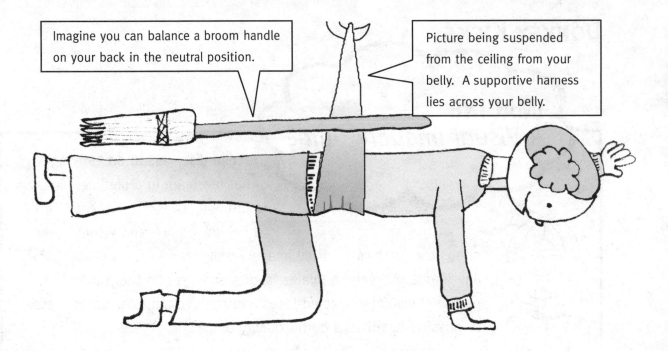

Imagine you can balance a broom handle on your back in the neutral position.

Picture being suspended from the ceiling from your belly. A supportive harness lies across your belly.

Step Two

- Inhale. Exhale as you straighten your right leg behind you. The right leg moves slowly with controlled momentum. The left arm also extends overhead. Your back returns to a neutral position.

You may also choose to bend the right leg and flex the foot when it moves behind you.

**is for
Alignment**

- Imagine you can balance a broom handle on your back in the neutral position. **See figure above.**

**is for
Breathing**

- You may choose to change the rhythm of your exhalations. It is helpful to let your air out in several rhythmic puffs in a row. EACH time you hear this breathing sound say to yourself, "contract my abdominals."

- Picture being suspended from the ceiling from your belly. A supportive harness lies across your belly. **See figure above.**

**is for
Control**

The harness is attached to the ceiling. At all times you must deepen your abdominal muscles inward toward your spine.

- Slowly kick your leg back. Visualize your upper, middle and lower glutes buttoning together.

CRAB DIPS

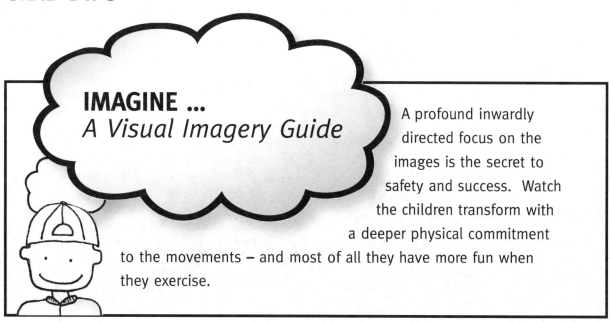

IMAGINE ...
A Visual Imagery Guide

A profound inwardly directed focus on the images is the secret to safety and success. Watch the children transform with a deeper physical commitment to the movements – and most of all they have more fun when they exercise.

The Crab Dip exercise may be done anywhere. It primarily strengthens the core and the tricep muscles located along the back of the arms.

TEACHING TIPS

Avoid if you have any shoulder, elbow, wrist or back problems.

- Perform 1-2 sets of 8-10 repetitions.

- The ABC Guide Boxes contain the visual imagery teaching cues. Say them out loud along with a reminder to breathe. You can't hear imagery cues enough. That way you won't fall into and out of proper form. Every repetition has to count.

POSITION

- Sit with your legs bent and the feet flat on the floor. Your arms are by your sides. The hands are next to your hips with the fingertips pointing to the sides of the room.

- Prepare before you move. Your legs are magnetized together. Feel your outer thighs drawing your inner thighs together. Continue to engage the muscles of your legs three-dimensionally. Use the front and back of your thighs, as well as your outer and inner thighs. Squeeze your glutes. Scoop your abdominals in, back AND up as if you are scooping out the front of your hips.

START

- Inhale. Exhale powerfully while you lift the hips off of the floor. Arms straighten.

- Bend and straighten your arms. Don't just lower and raise your hips. Keep the back of the neck long and the head supported on top of the spine.

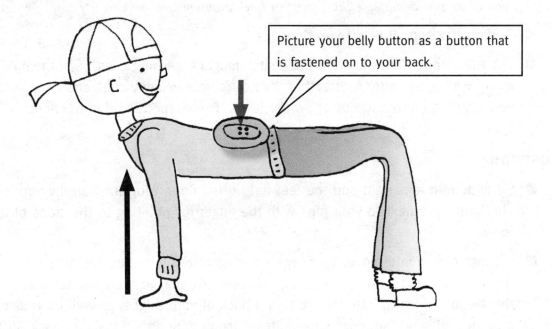

Picture your belly button as a button that is fastened on to your back.

is for
Alignment

■ Keep your entire
shoulder girdle area
organized. The
shoulders remain down
away from the ears. You
don't want to look like a
turtle coming out of its
shell.

is for
Breathing

■ Your breathing is
the key to help
you contract your
abdominals, glutes
and thighs. Always
make it your main
focus for EVERY
exercise.

is for
Control

■ Picture your belly button
as a button that is fas-
tened on to your back.
This image helps you to
keep scooping out your
pelvic abdominal area.
See figure on Page 44.
Also picture large but-
tons tightly fastening a
shirt closed.

Pilates Mat Exercises
Chapter Five

TEACHING TIPS

- Use a firm cushioned mat, blanket or carpet.

- The emphasis is never on the number of repetitions. Focus on the quality and slow rhythm of each movement. If you need to relax during the exercises, lie down and bring your legs in toward your chest.

- The essence of Pilates is the attention to details and essential principles of movement. Essential Alignment, Breathing and Core Control visual imagery cues are located in the ABC Guide Boxes. Focus on the imagery to bring all of the essential principles together. Your body will then move as an efficient unit. Keep your mind on the images and muscles to see results. Cultivate your own "inner coach" to constantly check every aspect of a movement. Pilates will then inspire you for a lifetime.

THE POWERHOUSE

Your focus is ALWAYS on the Powerhouse. The Powerhouse is the name Joseph Pilates gave to the abdominal area between the ribs and hips. The Powerhouse includes a large group of muscles in our center – the abdomen, lower back, hips, and buttocks. The Powerhouse is why your Core Control Visual Imagery Guide Boxes are so important.

THE BASE OF THE POWERHOUSE

The base of the Powerhouse is just as important as the Powerhouse. The base of the Powerhouse is often found using the "Pilates Stance." The Pilates Stance includes the pelvic floor muscles located at the base of the hips. Cough to feel the pelvic floor muscles. The Pilates Stance also includes the upper thigh and glutes.

THE PILATES STANCE POSITION

- The heels and legs are glued together.

- The feet are pointed, yet relaxed.

- Turn out your legs slightly. External rotation occurs within the hip joint.

- Tighten your glutes and wrap the back of the thighs toward each other.

THE HUNDRED

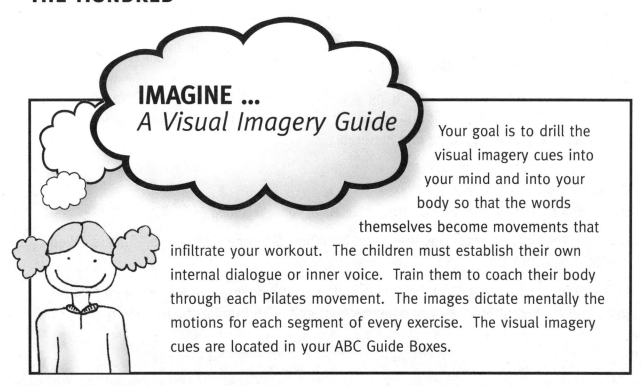

IMAGINE ...
A Visual Imagery Guide

Your goal is to drill the visual imagery cues into your mind and into your body so that the words themselves become movements that infiltrate your workout. The children must establish their own internal dialogue or inner voice. Train them to coach their body through each Pilates movement. The images dictate mentally the motions for each segment of every exercise. The visual imagery cues are located in your ABC Guide Boxes.

Avoid lifting the head if you have neck problems.

The exercise is called The Hundred because of the breathing rhythm.

- Take long, slow inhales for 5 counts. Then take long, slow exhales for 5 counts.

- Your goal is to build to 10 sets to equal a cycle of one hundred.

- For example, the teaching cue would be, "Inhale 2, 3, 4 5, Exhale 2, 3, 4, 5, Inhale 2, 3, 4, 5, Exhale 2, 3, 4, 5, etc."

POSITION

- Lie on your back. The legs are bent, feet flat. The heels are approximately 2 1/2 feet from your hips.

- One arm is straight by your side with the palm facing the floor. The other arm supports your head.

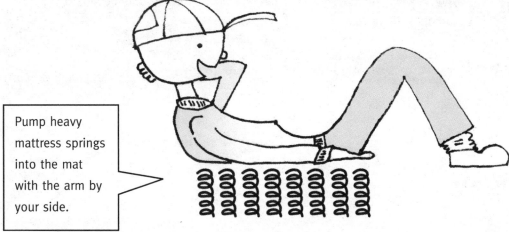

Pump heavy mattress springs into the mat with the arm by your side.

START

- Your arm supports the head as you bring the upper torso off the mat.

- Gaze at your navel. This reminds you to scoop your navel in toward the spine – whether you are inhaling or exhaling.

- Breathe in for 5 counts, pumping your arm up and down 5 times. Breathe out for 5 counts, pumping your arm up and down 5 times. This is one set. Build this to 10 sets, to equal a cycle of one hundred.

VARIATIONS

Leg Position for The Hundred Exercise When Your Powerhouse is Strong Enough

1. Lift the legs off the mat. Squeeze them together to form a right angle. This is called the "tabletop" position.

2. Straighten your legs toward the ceiling in the Pilates Stance. In Pilates Stance your legs are externally rotated as you squeeze your glutes and upper thighs together.

- Visualize your shoulder blades as wings sliding down the back.

- Pump heavy mattress springs into the mat

with the arm by your side. The arm helps you to keep the rhythm of your breathing. **See figure on Page 47.**

- To feel "neutral," simply lengthen your spine along the mat before you begin. Then concentrate on isolating your abdominal scoop without shifting your pelvis.

is for Alignment

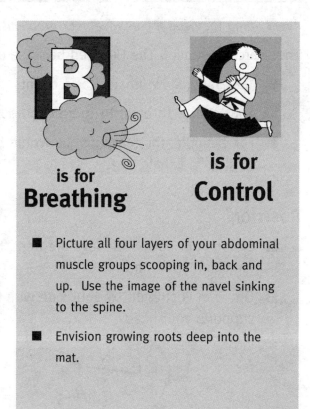

is for Breathing

is for Control

- Picture all four layers of your abdominal muscle groups scooping in, back and up. Use the image of the navel sinking to the spine.

- Envision growing roots deep into the mat.

THE ROLL-UP

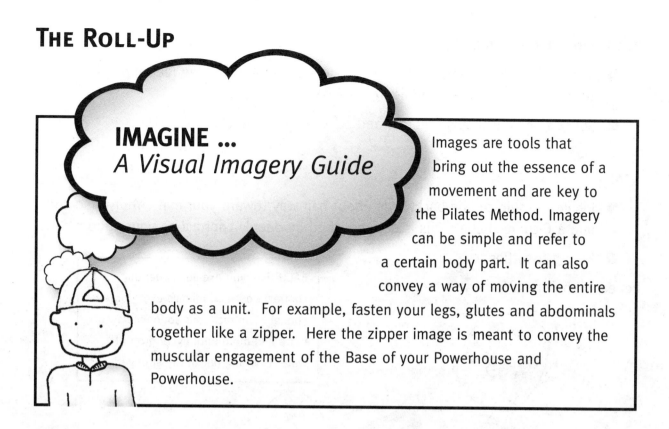

IMAGINE ...
A Visual Imagery Guide

Images are tools that bring out the essence of a movement and are key to the Pilates Method. Imagery can be simple and refer to a certain body part. It can also convey a way of moving the entire body as a unit. For example, fasten your legs, glutes and abdominals together like a zipper. Here the zipper image is meant to convey the muscular engagement of the Base of your Powerhouse and Powerhouse.

Avoid if you have any back problems.

The Roll-Up strengthens the abdominals to control spine articulation. You also gain flexibility in your hamstrings. It is recommended that you begin with a Half Roll-Up until your Powerhouse is very strong.

Picture your torso continuously curling over a huge water wheel of a windmill — while rolling up and down.

POSITION – HALF ROLL-UP

- Sit with your legs bent and the feet flat on the floor. Place the feet approximately 2 1/2 feet from your hips. **See figure on Page 49.**

- Super glue your thighs together and squeeze your glutes.

START

- Inhale. Exhale curling backwards about half way toward your mat. Your torso curls into a C-curve shape. This is accomplished by deeply contracting your abdominals.

- Return to sitting.

Repeat with perfect form 5-10 times.

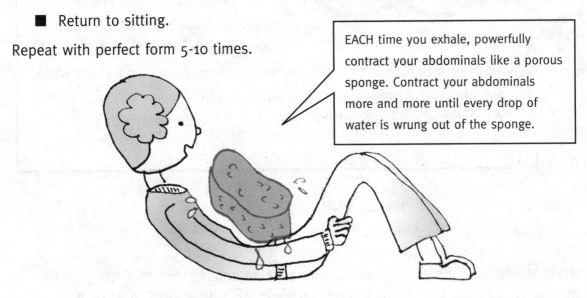

EACH time you exhale, powerfully contract your abdominals like a porous sponge. Contract your abdominals more and more until every drop of water is wrung out of the sponge.

POSITION – ROLL-UP

- Lie on your back. The legs are bent, feet flat on the mat approximately 2 1/2 feet from your hips. Hold on to the back of your thighs.

STEP ONE

- Inhale to prepare. Exhale, rolling up to sitting. Walk your hands along the back of your legs. This helps your spine form the letter C. This is referred to as a "C-Curve." The hands are helpful until your abdominals are strong enough to make the movements slow and controlled.

STEP TWO

- Inhale to prepare. Exhale, returning to your back the same way. Walk your hands along the back of your thighs toward your hips as you roll down.

Repeat 5-10 times.

LEG VARIATION FOR THE ROLL-UP

■ When your abdominals are strong enough, perform the Roll-Up in Pilates Stance. For example, the legs are extended along the mat. Externally rotate them slightly in the hip joint area. Squeeze the glutes and glue the back of your legs together – and into the mat.

■ The arms move from overhead to in front of you while rolling up and down. You may choose to support your head with one hand for the Roll Up.

is for
Alignment

Organize the feeling of your Pilates Stance using the following imagery: Feel your outer legs squeeze your inner legs together. Feel as if you can squeeze several tennis balls in between your legs – from your heels to your knees, thighs, and glutes. Keep your heels glued into the mat through-out the Roll-Up.

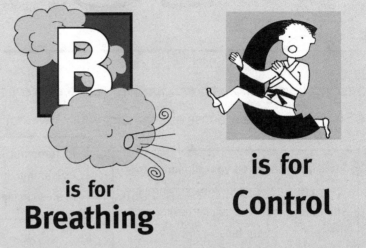

is for
Breathing

is for
Control

■ Picture your torso continuously curling over a huge water wheel of a windmill — while rolling up and down. This helps to find your C-Curve. It also helps you to contract your navel to the spine to keep the stomach away from the water wheel. **See figure on Page 49.**

■ EACH time you exhale, powerfully contract your abdominals like a porous sponge. Contract your abdominals more and more until every drop of water is wrung out of the sponge. Picture the sponge getting smaller and smaller inside your body. **See figure on Page 50.**

SINGLE LEG CIRCLES

IMAGINE ...
A Visual Imagery Guide

Visual imagery improves your precision and drives your concentration.

Avoid if you have any hip problems. You must keep the lower back on the mat.

The Single Leg Circle exercise strengthens your Powerhouse, hips and legs.

Place your hands on your hipbones to feel both sides of your hips staying very still on the mat. This is like having a 50 lb. weight on your hips.

Picture your leg as a paintbrush. Your foot is the brush. Imagine you have paint on your foot that makes circular brush strokes in the air.

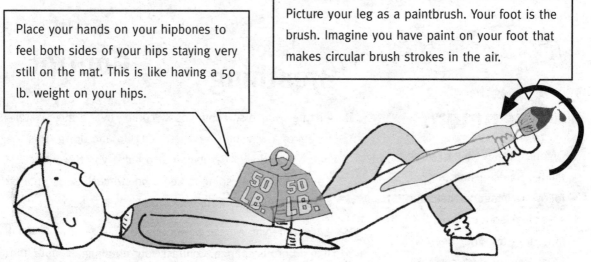

POSITION

- Lie on your back. Your left leg is either bent or straight in the Pilates Stance.

- Your right leg is in a central position with your toes aimed toward the ceiling. It is straight and slightly externally rotated from the hip joint.

- Lengthen and press the arms by your sides and into the mat.

START

- Inhale. Exhale while making a small circle with your right leg. The right leg moves across the body and then down, around and back up.

Repeat 10-15 times. Reverse the direction of the leg circle for 10-15 times. Change legs.

is for
Alignment

- Place your hands on your hipbones. This helps you feel both sides of your hips staying very still on the mat. This is like having a 50 lb. weight on your hips. **See figure on Page 52.**

- Picture your leg as a paintbrush. Your foot is the brush. Imagine you have paint on your foot that makes circular brush strokes in the air. **See figure on Page 52.**

is for
Breathing

is for
Control

- Breathe into the back of the rib cage. Visualize the gills of a fish to breathe into, located along the back of your ribs.

- On EVERY exhale, contract your deep abdominals like a powerful whirlpool swirling your navel into the floor.

- Squeeze your buttocks muscles so they form a pillow.

ROLLING LIKE A BALL

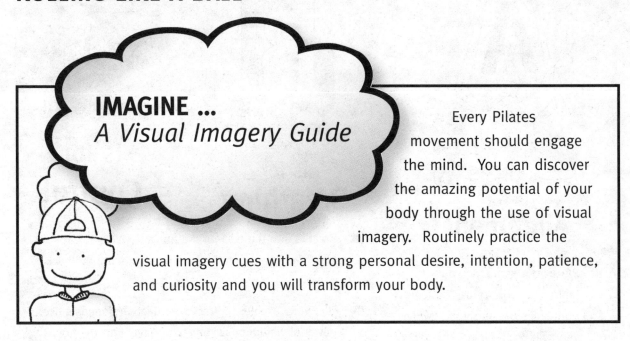

IMAGINE ...
A Visual Imagery Guide

Every Pilates movement should engage the mind. You can discover the amazing potential of your body through the use of visual imagery. Routinely practice the visual imagery cues with a strong personal desire, intention, patience, and curiosity and you will transform your body.

Rolling Like a Ball teaches balance and controlled momentum from your Powerhouse.

Avoid if you have back or neck problems.

POSITION

- Sit and balance behind your sit-bones in a C-Curve, with the feet off of the mat. Place your hands on your shins.

START
Step One

- Inhale. Exhale, maintaining a C-Curve shape with your trunk at all times.

- Roll backwards no further than the base of your shoulder blades.

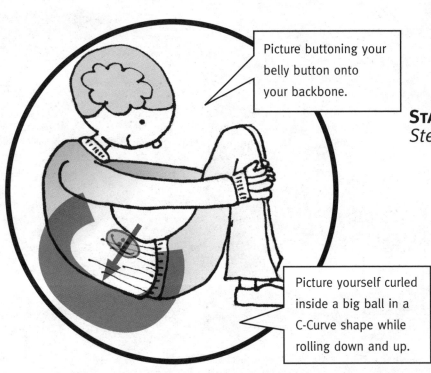

Picture buttoning your belly button onto your backbone.

Picture yourself curled inside a big ball in a C-Curve shape while rolling down and up.

Your back is in the shape of a scared Halloween cat.

Step Two

- Inhale. Exhale to roll forward to the starting position.

Repeat 10-15 times.

- Visualize your shirt tucked deep inside the waistband of your pants. This image keeps your shoulder girdle organized downward away from your ears. This improves deep abdominal support.

- Picture yourself curled inside a big ball in a C-Curve shape while rolling down and up. **See figure on Page 54.**

- Your back is in the shape of a scared Halloween cat. **See figure on Page 54.**

is for
Alignment

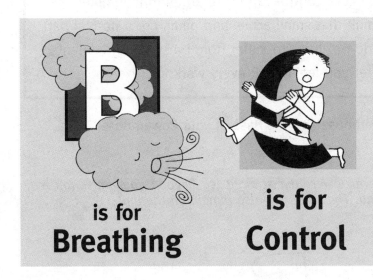

- EVERY time you hear yourself exhale, powerfully contract your Powerhouse more. Never let your abdominals relax. Picture buttoning your belly button onto your backbone. **See figure on Page 54.**

- Exhale, visualizing your abdominals as a plump raisin that shrivels more and more into a dried up raisin.

is for
Breathing

is for
Control

SINGLE LEG STRETCH

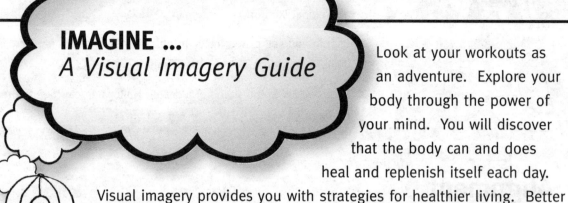

IMAGINE ...
A Visual Imagery Guide

Look at your workouts as an adventure. Explore your body through the power of your mind. You will discover that the body can and does heal and replenish itself each day.

Visual imagery provides you with strategies for healthier living. Better posture, breathing and core control can make an enormous difference in your health. We think that small aches and pains are a normal part of our lives. But we do not have to suffer from these minor ailments. Notice how much better you feel AFTER every workout.

Single Leg Stretch strengthens your Powerhouse and the Base of your Powerhouse.

Avoid if you have hip problems.

Gently place your hand on your knee. Never lower your straight leg beyond your hips. You may choose to support your head with one hand. The head can also remain on the mat.

POSITION

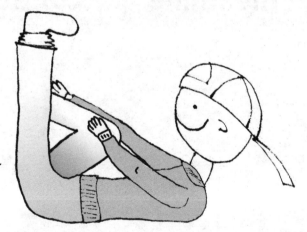

- Lie down on your back.
- Your left leg is straight toward the ceiling.
- Your right leg is bent toward your chest.
- Your left hand is on the inside of your right knee.
- Your right hand is on the outside of your right ankle.

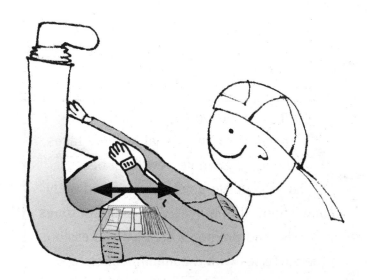

START

- Curl your upper trunk up off the mat.

- Inhale. Exhale, contracting your abdominals while you change legs and hands.

Perform 15 repetitions on each side.

You may want to support your head with one arm. After your Powerhouse strengthens, you may choose to lower your straight leg 60 degrees closer to the mat.

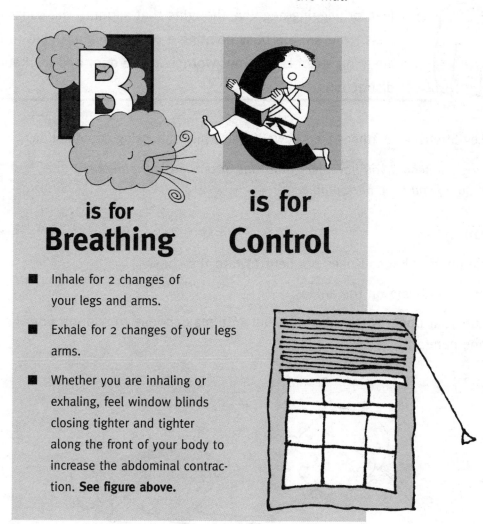

B is for Breathing

C is for Control

- Inhale for 2 changes of your legs and arms.

- Exhale for 2 changes of your legs arms.

- Whether you are inhaling or exhaling, feel window blinds closing tighter and tighter along the front of your body to increase the abdominal contraction. **See figure above.**

DOUBLE LEG STRETCH

IMAGINE ...
A Visual Imagery Guide

It is never too early to begin a fitness program. Visual imagery takes fitness to a whole new level because it harnesses the power of the mind-body connection. It improves your posture, tones your body, builds athletic skills, and promotes creative expression, health and healing. Do the exercises with a commitment to focus on the power of the imagination to stimulate your innate healing abilities. Creative visualization is a positive way to alleviate worry, fear, or nagging negative thoughts that slip into the consciousness. You are too busy painting a picture in your mind to think of anything else. Leave your worries at the door and workout without distractions.

Double Leg Stretch strengthens your Powerhouse while enhancing coordination.

Avoid lifting the head if you have neck problems or tension in the neck.
Don't perform if you have back problems.

POSITION

- Lie on your back. Knees are bent toward the chest.

- Your hands are on the ankles.

- Curl your upper trunk off of the mat. You may choose to support your head with one hand.

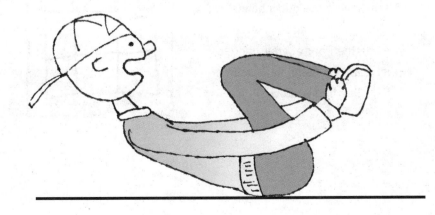

START
Step One

■ Inhale. Exhale, straightening your legs toward the ceiling at the same time your arms move overhead. Your legs are in the Pilates Stance.

Step Two

■ Inhale. Exhale, returning to the starting position.

Repeat 10 – 15 times.

LEG VARIATION FOR DOUBLE LEG STRETCH

When you improve your Powerhouse strength you may lower your legs approximately 60 degrees above the mat.

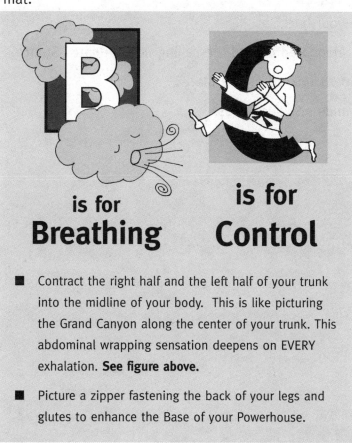

is for
Breathing

is for
Control

■ Contract the right half and the left half of your trunk into the midline of your body. This is like picturing the Grand Canyon along the center of your trunk. This abdominal wrapping sensation deepens on EVERY exhalation. **See figure above.**

■ Picture a zipper fastening the back of your legs and glutes to enhance the Base of your Powerhouse.

SINGLE STRAIGHT LEG STRETCH

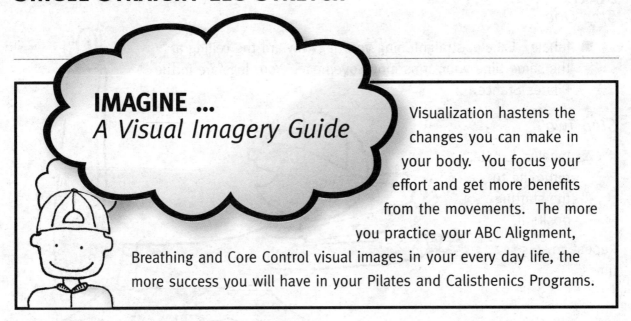

IMAGINE ...
A Visual Imagery Guide

Visualization hastens the changes you can make in your body. You focus your effort and get more benefits from the movements. The more you practice your ABC Alignment, Breathing and Core Control visual images in your every day life, the more success you will have in your Pilates and Calisthenics Programs.

The Single Straight Leg Stretch strengthens the Powerhouse and stretches the back of the legs.

Avoid if you have back problems.
Avoid lifting the head if you feel tension in the neck.

POSITION

- Lie down on your back.

- The legs are elongated toward the ceiling in the Pilates Stance.

- Curl your upper trunk up off the mat.

- Place your hands on your calves.

START

- Separate the legs while exhaling.

- The top leg pulses twice while you hold that calf with your hands. Stretch the bottom leg toward the wall in front of you.

Change legs. You may want to keep your knees bent.

Repeat 10 – 15 times.

- Picture yourself tucking an imaginary shirt deep into the waistband of your trousers. This image helps you to stabilize your shoulder girdle downward away from your ears.

- Powerfully close an imaginary belt around the trousers. This improves core control.

**is for
Alignment**

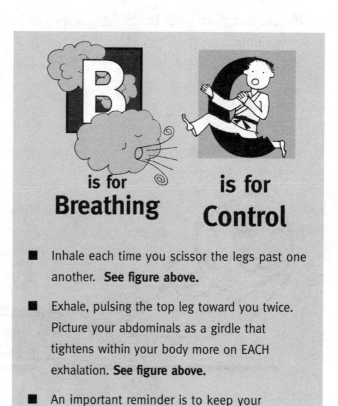

**is for
Breathing**

**is for
Control**

- Inhale each time you scissor the legs past one another. **See figure above.**

- Exhale, pulsing the top leg toward you twice. Picture your abdominals as a girdle that tightens within your body more on EACH exhalation. **See figure above.**

- An important reminder is to keep your abdominals engaged during your inhalations.

DOUBLE STRAIGHT LEG STRETCH

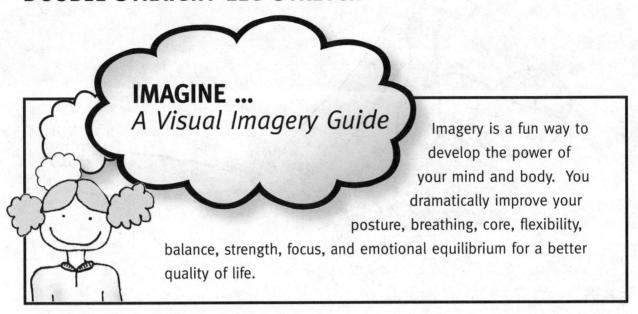

IMAGINE ...
A Visual Imagery Guide

Imagery is a fun way to develop the power of your mind and body. You dramatically improve your posture, breathing, core, flexibility, balance, strength, focus, and emotional equilibrium for a better quality of life.

The Double Straight Leg Stretch strengthens the Powerhouse. Until your Powerhouse is strong enough you may want to bend your legs. You can also place your hands beneath your hips.

Avoid if you have back problems.
Keep your head on the mat if you feel neck tension.

POSITION

- Lie down on your back. Your legs are in the Pilates Stance and pointed up to the ceiling.

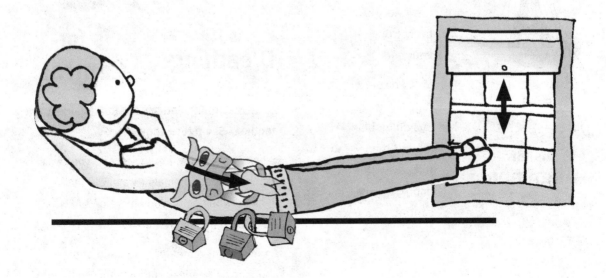

START

- Inhale. Exhale, curling your upper trunk off the mat. Support your head with your hands. You may also choose to keep your head on the mat.

Step One

- Inhale. Exhale, slowly lowering your legs a few inches toward the mat. Be sure that your lower back stays on the mat.

Step Two

- Inhale. Exhale and return your legs a bit faster to the starting position.

Repeat 10 – 15 times with perfect form.

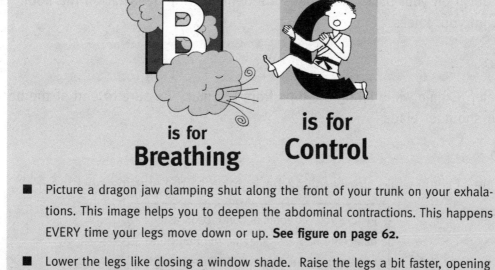

B is for Breathing

C is for Control

- Picture a dragon jaw clamping shut along the front of your trunk on your exhalations. This image helps you to deepen the abdominal contractions. This happens EVERY time your legs move down or up. **See figure on page 62.**

- Lower the legs like closing a window shade. Raise the legs a bit faster, opening the window shade. **See figure on page 62.**

- Lock your hips, lower back, and middle back against the mat. **See figure on page 62.**

BRIDGE/HINGE

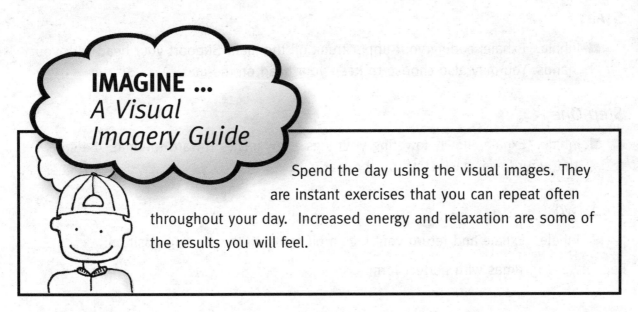

IMAGINE ...
*A Visual
Imagery Guide*

Spend the day using the visual images. They are instant exercises that you can repeat often throughout your day. Increased energy and relaxation are some of the results you will feel.

The Bridge/Hinge strengthens the Powerhouse, thighs, glutes and back.

Avoid if you have back, abdominal or hip problems.

POSITION

- Lie down on your back. The knees are bent with the feet flat on the floor. Gaze toward your knees.

START
Step One

- Inhale. Exhale while lifting the hips from the mat. Be sure to end at the base of your shoulder blades.

Step Two

- Inhale. Exhale while slowly rolling back down to the starting position.

Repeat 3 – 8 times.

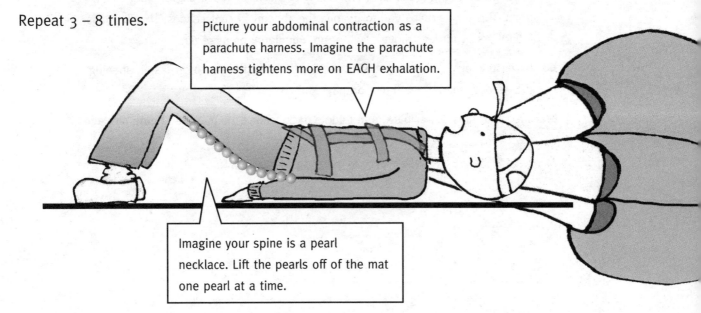

Picture your abdominal contraction as a parachute harness. Imagine the parachute harness tightens more on EACH exhalation.

Imagine your spine is a pearl necklace. Lift the pearls off of the mat one pearl at a time.

is for
Alignment

■ Imagine your spine is a
pearl necklace. Lift the
pearls off of the mat one
pearl at a time. **See figure
on Page 64.**

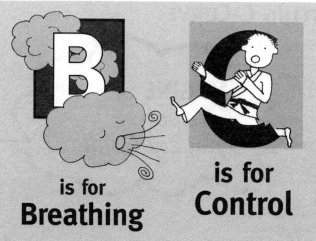

is for
Breathing

is for
Control

■ Picture your abdominal contraction as a parachute
harness. Imagine the parachute harness tightens
more on EACH exhalation. This image helps you to
defy gravity as you hover above the mat. It is also
a reminder to squeeze the glutes and contract your
abdominals. **See figure on Page 64.**

SITTING C-CURVE

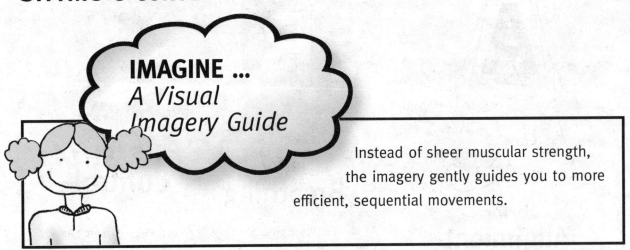

IMAGINE ...
A Visual Imagery Guide

Instead of sheer muscular strength, the imagery gently guides you to more efficient, sequential movements.

The Sitting C-Curve strengthens the Powerhouse and stretches the upper back and hamstrings.

Avoid if you have back problems.

POSITION

- Sit with the legs extended and slightly apart. Flex the feet.
- The arms are straight in front of you at shoulder level with the palms facing the mat.

Roll your spine up like stacking the vertebras one by one as if a wall were right behind you.

Picture your trunk curling over a huge nautilus seashell. Keep your abdominals scooped up and away from the shell.

START
Step One

- Inhale. Exhale, sinking your navel to your spine. Move your trunk as if making the letter C. The head moves first.

Step Two

- Inhale. Exhale while rolling up. The head comes up last.

Repeat 3 – 5 times.

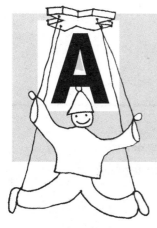

- Picture your trunk curling over a huge nautilus seashell. Keep your abdominals scooped up and away from the shell. **See figure on Page 66.**

- Roll your spine up, stacking the vertebras one by one as if a wall were right behind you. **See figure on Page 66.**

is for
Alignment

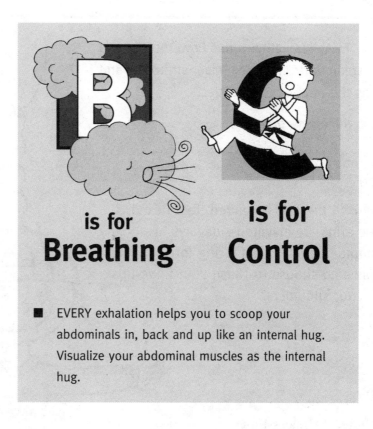

is for
Breathing

is for
Control

- EVERY exhalation helps you to scoop your abdominals in, back and up like an internal hug. Visualize your abdominal muscles as the internal hug.

SITTING TWIST

IMAGINE ...
A Visual Imagery Guide

Visual imagery provides us with the ability to live in our body with suppleness, strength and emotional calmness.

The Sitting Twist strengthens the Powerhouse and improves spine articulation. It also stretches and strengthens the upper back muscles.

Avoid if you have back problems.

Picture a helium balloon attached to the ceiling from the top of your head. This image keeps your trunk elongated.

POSITION

■ Sit with the legs extended, feet flexed. The arms are elevated sideways at shoulder level, palms facing forward. You may also choose to touch your fingertips to your shoulders.

START
Step One

■ Inhale. Exhale 3 times rotating the trunk to the right (rotate a little further with each exhalation).

Stack your pelvis, ribs, chest and head on top of each other like building blocks.

Step Two

■ Inhale, returning to the starting position.

Repeat 3 – 5 times to each side.

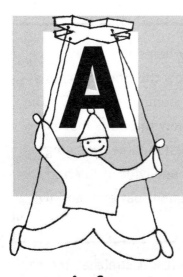

is for
Alignment

- Stack your pelvis, ribs, chest and head on top of each other like building blocks. Picture a helium balloon attached to the ceiling from the top of your head. These images keep your trunk elongated. **See figures on Page 68.**

- Keep your hipbones facing forward like two headlights on a car. Turn from above the waist while contracting the abdominals.

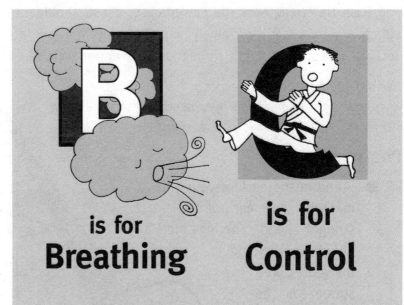

is for
Breathing

is for
Control

- On EVERY three exhales, contract your abdominals like a wet rag. This feels like the rag is wrung out more and more and more. Cinch the front of your ribs together.

- Also sink your navel to the spine to activate your Pilates Scoop.

PILATES PUSH UP

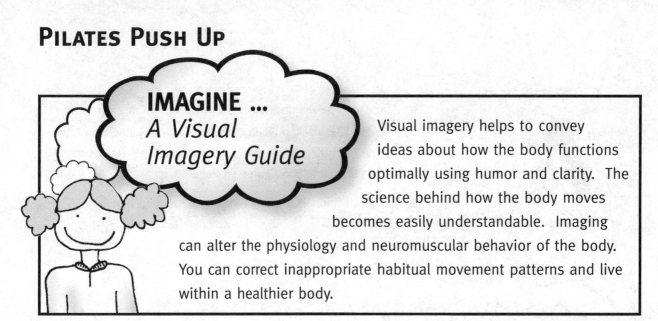

IMAGINE ...
A Visual Imagery Guide

Visual imagery helps to convey ideas about how the body functions optimally using humor and clarity. The science behind how the body moves becomes easily understandable. Imaging can alter the physiology and neuromuscular behavior of the body. You can correct inappropriate habitual movement patterns and live within a healthier body.

The Push Up strengthens the Powerhouse, chest, shoulders and glutes. It stretches the hamstrings and calves. It is extremely helpful to place a 6 to 8 inch ball between your upper thighs. You will hug the ball tightly throughout this entire exercise.

Avoid if you have back, shoulder or hip problems.
Keep your wrist aligned directly beneath the shoulder joint.

POSITION

- Stand at the back of your mat with your feet pointed straight ahead. The legs are glued together and the glutes are squeezed. The arms are by your sides.

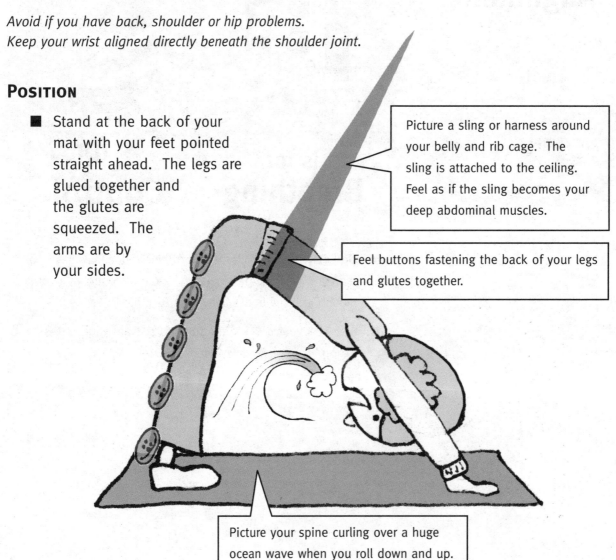

Picture a sling or harness around your belly and rib cage. The sling is attached to the ceiling. Feel as if the sling becomes your deep abdominal muscles.

Feel buttons fastening the back of your legs and glutes together.

Picture your spine curling over a huge ocean wave when you roll down and up.

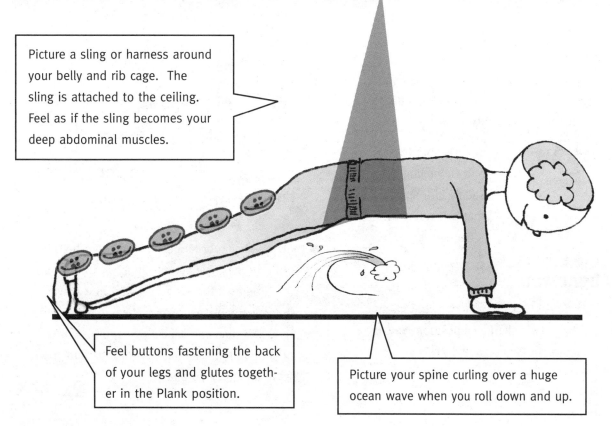

Picture a sling or harness around your belly and rib cage. The sling is attached to the ceiling. Feel as if the sling becomes your deep abdominal muscles.

Feel buttons fastening the back of your legs and glutes together in the Plank position.

Picture your spine curling over a huge ocean wave when you roll down and up.

START
Step One

■ Inhale. Exhale while curling the trunk forward. Walk the hands down the front of the legs until the fingers reach the floor.

Step Two

■ Inhale. Exhale as the hands walk out to the front of the mat.

Step Three

■ Inhale. Exhale, aligning the body in a Plank Push Up position.

Step Four

■ Inhale as your chest lowers toward the mat. Exhale, returning to Plank. You may choose to do a bent knee position for the Push Up.

Step Five

■ Inhale. Exhale as the hands walk back toward the feet.

Step Six

■ Inhale. Exhale as the spine articulates walking the hands back up the front of the legs.

Repeat 3 – 5 times.

- Picture your spine curling over a huge ocean wave when you roll down and up. **See figure on Page 71.**

is for
Alignment

- Feel your legs and glutes hug the saddle of a horse that is jumping over a fence.

- Feel buttons fastening the back of your legs and glutes together in the Plank position. **See figure on Pages 70 and 71.**

is for
Breathing

is for
Control

- Picture a sling or harness around your belly and rib cage. The sling is attached to the ceiling. Feel as if the sling becomes your deep abdominal muscles. Scoop them in, back and up EVERY time you exhale powerfully. Don't let your abdominals relax toward the floor. **See figure on Pages 70 and 71.**

Wall Stretches

Chapter Six

TEACHING TIPS FOR THE ART OF STRETCHING

- The Wall Stretches are first and foremost practical exercises. Anytime you have a wall you can stretch.

- To increase flexibility, it is critical to have warm muscles during the stretching exercises. For maximum results, stretch immediately AFTER the calisthenic or Pilates exercise session. Otherwise, walk vigorously in place for 5 minutes to warm-up BEFORE you stretch.

- Hold each stretch statically (no bouncing). These days a new generation of teachers has the opportunity to teach children how to take care of themselves. Learning how to stretch properly can help provide a positive attitude toward staying healthy for the rest of their lives. Stretching after workouts, sports and recreational activities can prevent muscle soreness, overuse syndromes, injury and burn out.

- Perform 3-5 repetitions of each Wall Stretch, holding for 20-30 seconds.

- Relax the muscle group being stretched. Stretch each muscle group to the point of slight comfortable tension.

- It is not important how far you go in a stretch but rather how it feels while you're in a stretch.

- Balloon Breathing is the key to becoming supple. Read Chapter Two for a reminder about Balloon Breathing. Pay attention to the images in the Breathing Guide Boxes.

HANDS UP THE WALL

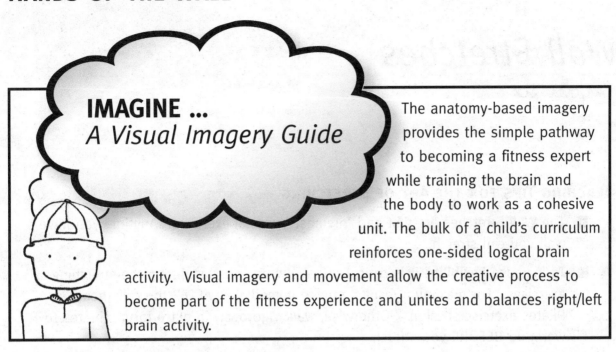

IMAGINE ...
A Visual Imagery Guide

The anatomy-based imagery provides the simple pathway to becoming a fitness expert while training the brain and the body to work as a cohesive unit. The bulk of a child's curriculum reinforces one-sided logical brain activity. Visual imagery and movement allow the creative process to become part of the fitness experience and unites and balances right/left brain activity.

Hands Up the Wall stretches the chest, arms and abdominals.

Avoid if you have back or arm problems.

POSITION

- Stand facing the wall. You are approximately one foot away from the wall.

- Place your palms flat on the wall in line with your shoulders.

Picture a long dinosaur tail from your tailbone to the floor.

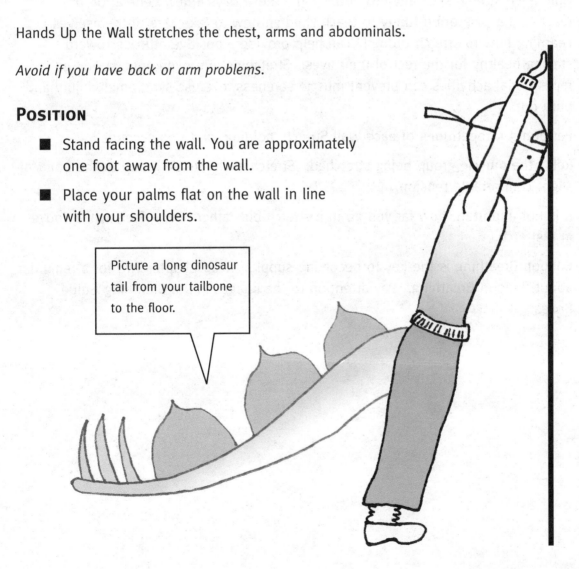

■ Slowly slide the hands overhead until your face is next to the wall.

■ Keep your stomach in, tailbone dropped. Don't stick your bottom out. Gently stretch up the wall. Hold the stretch while you take long, slow breaths.

Repeat the exercise 3-5 times.

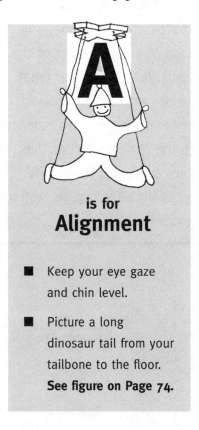

**is for
Alignment**

■ Keep your eye gaze and chin level.

■ Picture a long dinosaur tail from your tailbone to the floor. **See figure on Page 74.**

**is for
Breathing**

■ Picture gradually filling a hot air balloon inside of you on each inhalation. It deflates on the exhalations.

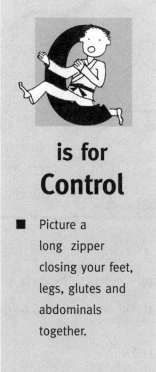

**is for
Control**

■ Picture a long zipper closing your feet, legs, glutes and abdominals together.

TABLETOP

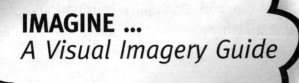

IMAGINE ...
A Visual Imagery Guide

The visual imagery provides simplicity and reinforces the practical anytime, any-place traveling aspect of the fitness program. No matter what circumstance a child finds himself in, he can tap into his "inner environment" through the visual imagery to gain strength, balance, coordination and relaxation. Encourage the children to practice... practice...practice their ABC visual imagery cues with their daily activities. For example, walking, biking, skate boarding, as well as standing in long lines, sitting and lying down.

Tabletop stretches the back of the thigh, upper back and back of the arm.

Avoid if you have any leg, arm or back problems.

POSITION

- ■ Step 2-3 feet away from the wall.

- ■ Stand with the feet shoulder-width apart.

- ■ Bend at the hip and place the hands on the wall. The knees are slightly bent. Your back remains flat like a tabletop.

> Your back is flat and level. You could serve tea on your back.

> Direct your air into an imaginary balloon located in your trunk. On each exhalation, picture the balloon deflating.

> Plant your feet into the floor like roots of a tree.

START

- ■ Inhale. Exhale and slightly contract your abdominals toward your spine. Gently press your shoulders and chest toward the floor.

Repeat the exercise 3 times.

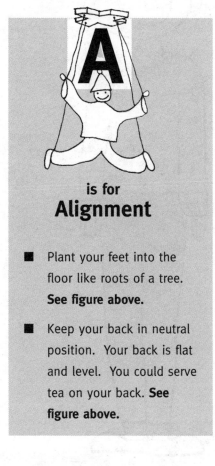

is for
Alignment

- ■ Plant your feet into the floor like roots of a tree. **See figure above.**

- ■ Keep your back in neutral position. Your back is flat and level. You could serve tea on your back. **See figure above.**

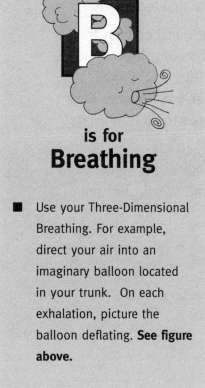

is for
Breathing

- ■ Use your Three-Dimensional Breathing. For example, direct your air into an imaginary balloon located in your trunk. On each exhalation, picture the balloon deflating. **See figure above.**

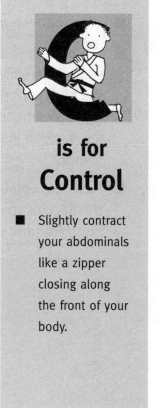

is for
Control

- ■ Slightly contract your abdominals like a zipper closing along the front of your body.

WALL ROLL DOWN

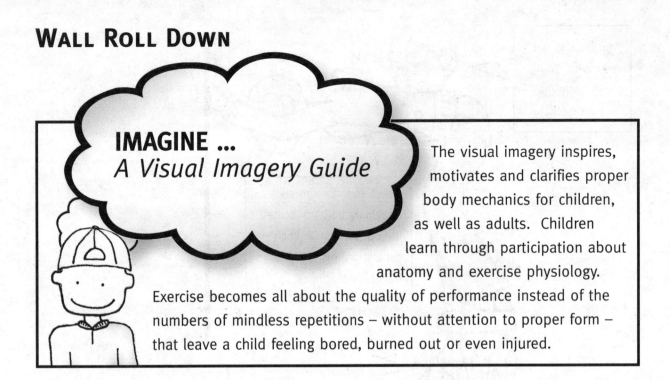

IMAGINE ...
A Visual Imagery Guide

The visual imagery inspires, motivates and clarifies proper body mechanics for children, as well as adults. Children learn through participation about anatomy and exercise physiology. Exercise becomes all about the quality of performance instead of the numbers of mindless repetitions – without attention to proper form – that leave a child feeling bored, burned out or even injured.

The Wall Roll Down is a spinal articulation exercise. It also stretches the hamstrings located along the back of the thighs. You have to engage your core in order to work against gravity's downward pull.

Avoid if you have any back, neck or leg problems.

POSITION

- Stand with your back against a wall.

- Place the feet about 8 inches from the wall. Externally rotate your legs from the hip joint area. Glue your thighs together and squeeze your glutes. This leg position is referred to as the "Pilates stance."

- Press the entire length of the spine, from the back of your head to your bottom, firmly into the wall.

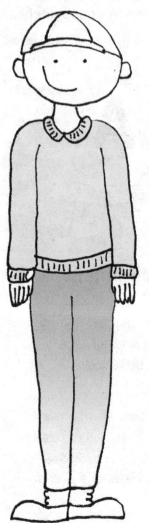

START
Step One

- Inhale. Exhale and treat the entire spine as one unit as you begin to peel off of the wall. The head moves first, then the shoulders. Relax the arms loosely at your sides.

- Continue to pull the waist up and feel your lower back pushing the wall away.

Step Two

- Peel the ribs off the wall but pull the navel up higher. Allow your bottom to move up the wall. Lengthen the torso. Touch the spine at the back of the waist. Allow the back to round down very gently. Aim the top of the head to the floor. Hang and breathe.

Step Three

- Slowly curl back up the wall. Curl up vertebra by vertebra. You may want to place your hands on your thighs.

Repeat the exercise 3-5 times.

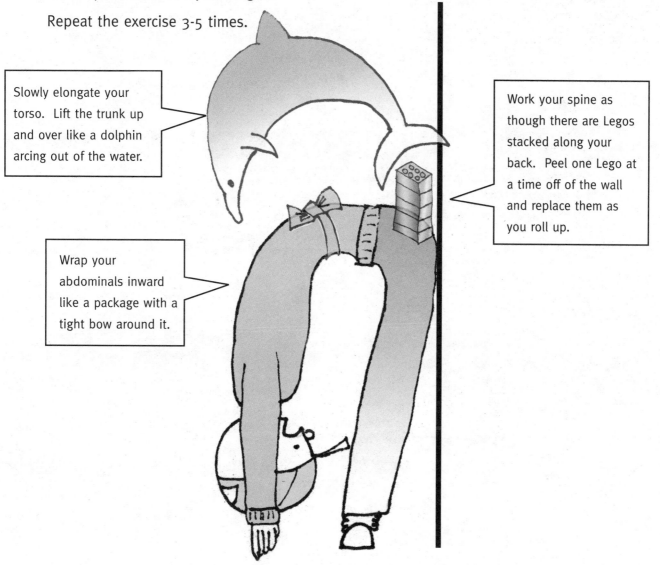

Slowly elongate your torso. Lift the trunk up and over like a dolphin arcing out of the water.

Work your spine as though there are Legos stacked along your back. Peel one Lego at a time off of the wall and replace them as you roll up.

Wrap your abdominals inward like a package with a tight bow around it.

- Work your spine as though there are Legos stacked along your back. Peel one Lego at a time off of the wall and replace them as you roll up. **See figure on Page 79.**

- Slowly elongate your torso. Lift the trunk up and over like a dolphin arcing out of the water. **See figure on Page 79.**

is for
Alignment

is for
Breathing

is for
Control

- Breathe steadily. EVERY time you hear yourself exhale it is a reminder to contract the abdominals.

- Wrap your abdominals inward like a package with a tight bow around it. **See figure on Page 79.**

CALF STRETCH

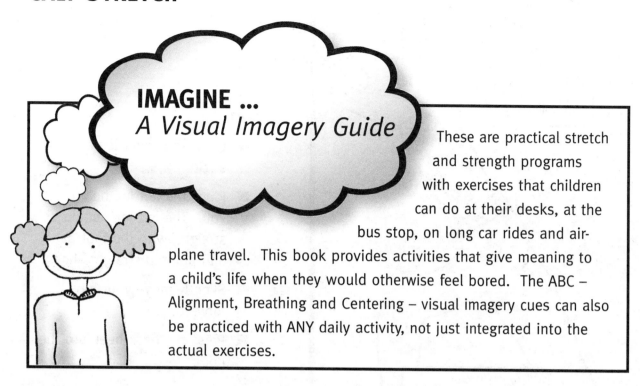

IMAGINE ...
A Visual Imagery Guide

These are practical stretch and strength programs with exercises that children can do at their desks, at the bus stop, on long car rides and airplane travel. This book provides activities that give meaning to a child's life when they would otherwise feel bored. The ABC – Alignment, Breathing and Centering – visual imagery cues can also be practiced with ANY daily activity, not just integrated into the actual exercises.

The Calf Stretch primarily stretches the back of the lower leg.

Avoid if you have any leg or Achilles tendon problems.

POSITION

- Stand. Lean forward against the wall, resting on the forearms. Cross one hand over the other.

- Rest your forehead on the back of your hands. Keep your eye gaze level.

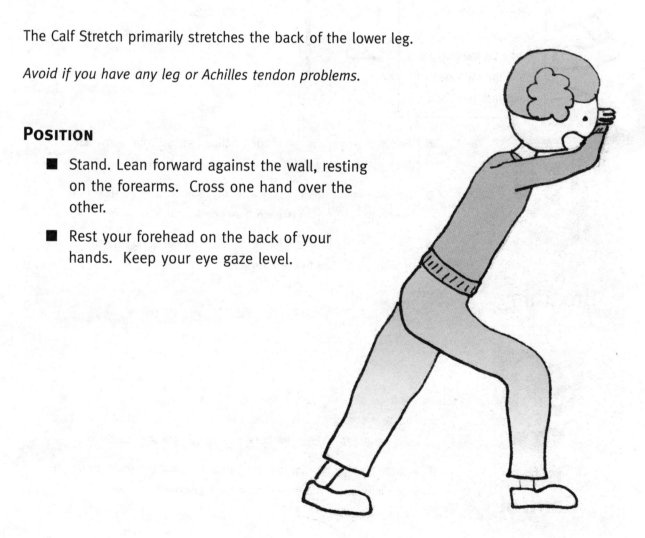

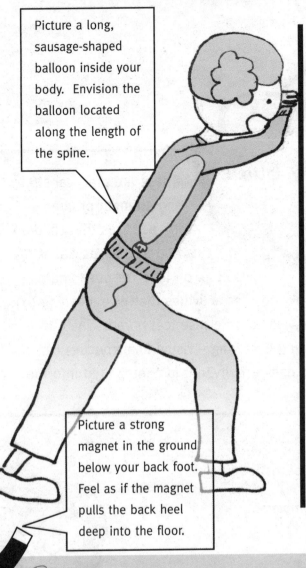

Picture a long, sausage-shaped balloon inside your body. Envision the balloon located along the length of the spine.

Picture a strong magnet in the ground below your back foot. Feel as if the magnet pulls the back heel deep into the floor.

START

- Bend your right leg at a right angle.

- Place the left leg behind you. The left leg should be straight, with the foot flat and pointed straight ahead.

- Slightly move your hips forward.

- Press the back heel into the floor.

Change legs.

B is for Breathing

- Picture a long, sausage-shaped balloon inside your body. Envision the balloon located along the length of the spine.

- Visualize filling this balloon with air up and down vertically. It lengthens and expands each time you inhale.

- Each time you exhale, picture the balloon deflating into the center of your body. **See figure above.**

is for Control

- Picture a strong magnet in the ground below your back foot. Feel as if the magnet pulls the back heel deep into the floor.

- Picture sending all four layers of your abdominal muscle groups to your backbone. This happens when you exhale.

FOOT ON THE WALL

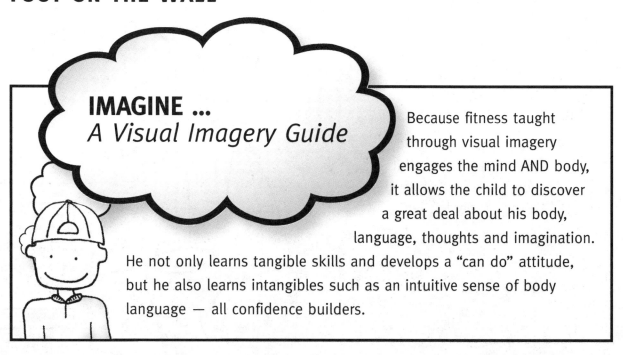

IMAGINE ...
A Visual Imagery Guide

Because fitness taught through visual imagery engages the mind AND body, it allows the child to discover a great deal about his body, language, thoughts and imagination.

He not only learns tangible skills and develops a "can do" attitude, but he also learns intangibles such as an intuitive sense of body language — all confidence builders.

Avoid if you have any foot or Achilles tendon problems.

Foot on the Wall stretches the bottom of the foot and toes. It also stretches the Achilles tendon area.

POSITION

- Stand facing the wall. Straighten your left leg. Place your left foot against the wall. Your left ankle is flexed and the ball and toes of the foot touch the wall. The left heel is on the floor.

- Your right leg is bent behind you. You may have to lift the right heel off the floor.

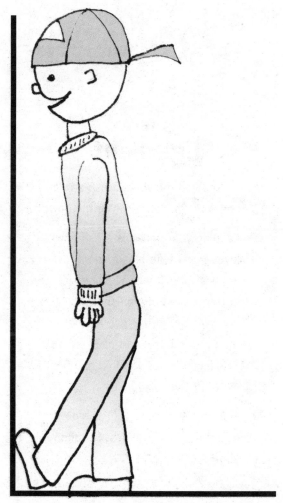

Start

■ Move your upper body and hips forward until you feel a mild stretch on the lower left leg.

Change to the other leg.

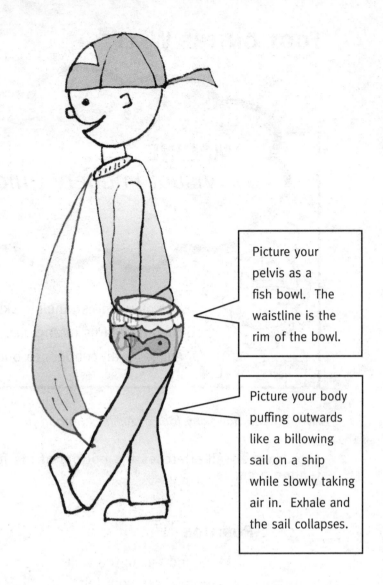

Picture your pelvis as a fish bowl. The waistline is the rim of the bowl.

Picture your body puffing outwards like a billowing sail on a ship while slowly taking air in. Exhale and the sail collapses.

is for
Alignment

■ Picture your pelvis as a fish bowl. The waistline is the rim of the bowl.

■ Keeping your pelvis as a fish bowl level, move your hips forward toward the wall. Don't let any water slosh out of the rim of the fish bowl. Also don't let any of the fish flop out on the floor in front or in back of you. This image helps you find and feel a neutral pelvic posture.

■ Engage the back of your fish bowl by squeezing the glutes. **See figure above.**

is for
Breathing

■ Picture your body puffing outwards like a billowing sail on a ship while slowly taking air in. Exhale and the sail collapses.

THIGH STRETCH

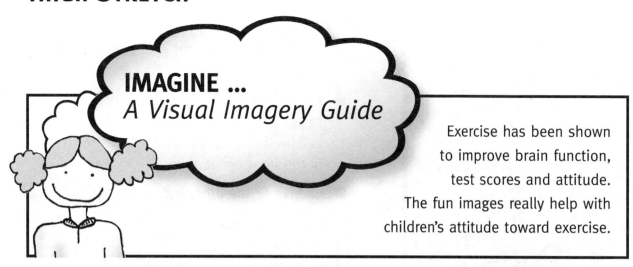

IMAGINE ...
A Visual Imagery Guide

Exercise has been shown to improve brain function, test scores and attitude. The fun images really help with children's attitude toward exercise.

The Thigh Stretch stretches the front of the thigh and hip flexors.

Avoid if you have any leg or back problems. Keep the front of your hip open.

POSITION

- Stand facing the wall. Keep your eye gaze level.

- Keep your left hand on the wall for support during the stretch.

- While keeping your right support leg slightly bent, hold the top of the right foot with your right hand.

START

- Gently draw your right heel toward your bottom.

- Keep both knees and thighs close together. Tighten the glutes to fully extend the hips until you feel a stretch in the front of the thigh.

- Change to the other leg.

Inhale, directing your air up and down along your spine like an elevator moving between floors.

Plant your standing leg/ foot like roots into the floor. Picture the roots intertwining deep into the dirt.

- Inhale, directing your air up and down along your spine like an elevator moving between floors. **See figure above.**

is for Breathing

- Plant your standing leg/foot like roots into the floor. Picture the roots intertwining deep into the dirt. **See figure above.**

- Visualize strong vines from the Amazon wrapping around your body and reaching upward toward the sun.

is for Control

Chest Stretch

IMAGINE ...
*A Visual
Imagery Guide*

Visual imagery produces maximum functioning – a body that moves with ease and efficiency.

The Chest Stretch stretches the chest, arms and front of the shoulders.

Avoid if you have any arm, shoulder or back problems.

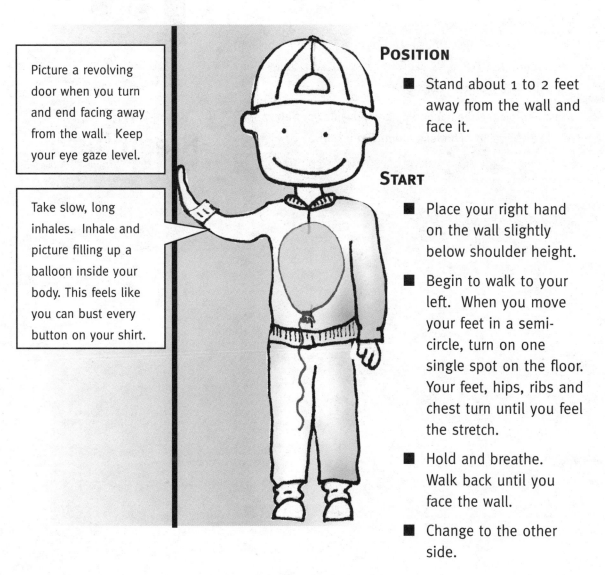

Picture a revolving door when you turn and end facing away from the wall. Keep your eye gaze level.

Take slow, long inhales. Inhale and picture filling up a balloon inside your body. This feels like you can bust every button on your shirt.

Position

- Stand about 1 to 2 feet away from the wall and face it.

Start

- Place your right hand on the wall slightly below shoulder height.

- Begin to walk to your left. When you move your feet in a semi-circle, turn on one single spot on the floor. Your feet, hips, ribs and chest turn until you feel the stretch.

- Hold and breathe. Walk back until you face the wall.

- Change to the other side.

- Picture a revolving door when you turn and end facing away from the wall. Keep your eye gaze level. **See figure on Page 87.**

- Picture your shoulder girdle as a shirt hung wide on a clothesline.

is for
Alignment

is for
Breathing

- Take slow, long inhales. Inhale and picture filling up a balloon inside your body. This feels like you can bust every button on your shirt. **See figure on Page 87.**

- Exhale and picture the balloon deflating inside your body. This feels like your shirt tightening around your body.

SIDEWAYS STRETCH

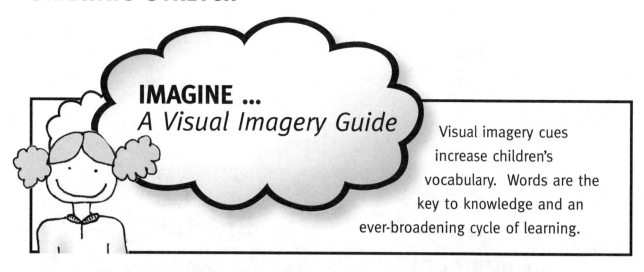

IMAGINE ...
A Visual Imagery Guide

Visual imagery cues increase children's vocabulary. Words are the key to knowledge and an ever-broadening cycle of learning.

The Sideways Stretch stretches the waistline and sides of your body.

Avoid if you have any back or neck problems.
Be careful if you have shoulder issues.

POSITION

- Stand sideways to a wall. You are 2 feet away from the wall with your right side toward it.

- Your feet are shoulder-width apart with the knees slightly bent.

START

- Place your right hand on the wall at about waist height.

- Now reach over your head with your left arm.

- To stretch your waistline and sides, move your trunk sideways toward the wall.

- Hold and breathe.

- Repeat 3-5 times.

- Change to the other side.

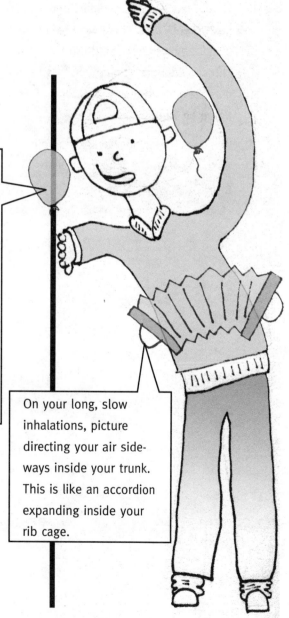

Picture having two imaginary balloons next to your ears. This image keeps your shoulder girdle muscles down and stable. The shoulders don't hike upwards to the ears even with the arm overhead.

On your long, slow inhalations, picture directing your air sideways inside your trunk. This is like an accordion expanding inside your rib cage.

is for
Alignment

- Picture having two imaginary balloons next to your ears. This image keeps your shoulder girdle muscles down and stable. The shoulders don't hike upwards to the ears even with the arm overhead. **See figure on Page 89.**

- When you bend sideways, keep your torso between two imaginary panes of glass.

is for
Breathing

- On your long, slow inhalations, picture directing your air sideways inside your trunk. This is like an accordion expanding inside your rib cage.

- The accordion folds back together on your exhalations. This helps you engage the abdominal muscles in the front of the ribs. **See figure on Page 89.**

LEGS ON THE WALL

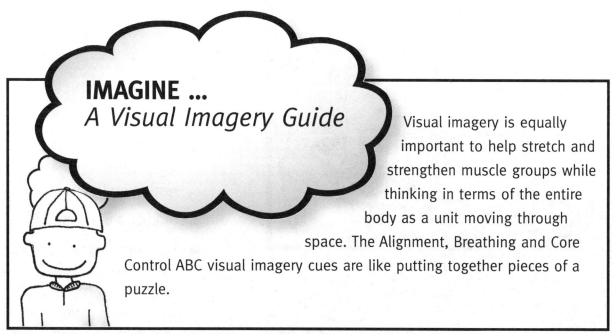

IMAGINE ...
A Visual Imagery Guide

Visual imagery is equally important to help stretch and strengthen muscle groups while thinking in terms of the entire body as a unit moving through space. The Alignment, Breathing and Core Control ABC visual imagery cues are like putting together pieces of a puzzle.

The Legs on the Wall stretch is for the hips and legs.

Avoid if you have any hip, leg or back problems. Modify if you have hip or groin problems.

POSITION

- Sit sideways next to a wall.

- Lie down gently onto your back.

- Slide your legs up onto the wall, resting on the heels.

- You are lying on your back with your bottom about 3-5 inches away from the wall. This keeps your lower back flat and not arched or off the floor.

- Your legs are elevated, straight and close together on the wall.

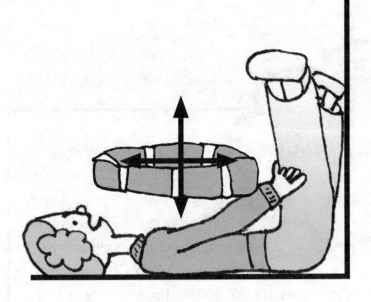

START

- Slowly separate your legs, with your heels resting on the wall.

- Hold and breathe.

- You may choose to place your hands on your outer thighs to keep the stretch comfortable. This is also helpful when you bring the legs back together.

- Curl onto your side on the floor and gradually return to sitting.

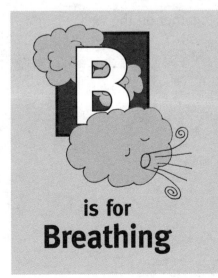

B

is for Breathing

- Picture a floating water raft gradually inflating within your trunk on your inhalations. Direct your intake of air up and down, sideways and forward and back until your raft puffs outward.

- Exhale, visualizing the imaginary floating raft deflating within your trunk. **See figure above.**

Benefits of Stretching

■ Stretching is first and foremost a great way to manage stress. Stretching is an opportunity to slow down and take care of yourself.

■ Conscious awareness of your breathing during a stretch creates more lasting benefits. Bring your focus back to your breathing if your mind wanders. Notice how supple you become on your long, slow exhalations. Relax and give into gravity.

■ Individual differences in a person's flexibility depends upon genetics, daily movement habits, posture, emotional stress and movement activities.

■ Stretching is essential to anyone involved in vigorous physical activity. It alleviates sore muscles. It speeds up recuperation time after physical exertion. It enhances fitness, sports, dance and martial arts performance by improving neuromuscular coordination. It helps to prevent burnout, overuse syndromes and injuries.

■ Stretching improves concentration.

■ Stretching pinpoints tight muscles and increases the quantity of synovial fluid within our joints.

■ Stretching enhances the body's blood and nutrient supply. It calms the nerves. Stretching gives a sense of vitality. Tense muscles have more toxicity and can cause lethargy.

Glossary

Abdominal Muscles: These muscles attach to your rib cage and your pelvis. There are four groups of abdominals. They are the rectus abdominis, external obliques, internal obliques, and transversus abdominis.

Armor or Image for Core Control: The physical and mental act of the abdominals contracting to support the body. Visualize your ribcage as a malleable, protective shield of armor. The armor cinches together in front to help you expel air and support the spine.

Balloon Breathing: This is a deep relaxation diaphragmatic breathing technique. It uses visualization to produce efficient breathing. The mental and physical act of exercising your breathing muscles – the diaphragm, chest and ribs – increases lung capacity. It replaces the habit of shallow chest breathing with deep diaphragmatic breathing. It is the key to stretching and stress management.

Base of the Powerhouse: These muscles must be activated for each Pilates movement. They include the leg, pelvic floor and buttocks muscles. Engagement of these muscles provides the ability to find deeper abdominal Powerhouse support.

C-Curve: Your head and torso form the letter C when you round or curl into flexion. The abdominals are responsible for maintaining this C-Curve shape during Pilates exercises.

Center, or Centering: The center is referred to as the Powerhouse in Pilates. All efficient and powerful motion ideally originates from the center. The body has a physical center, which includes the abdominals, back, hips, and buttocks muscles. Your Pilates and calisthenics exercises focus on strengthening this area to support the organs and spine. The result is a physical sense of confidence and better posture.

Core: The core includes your trunk muscles: the abdominal, back and buttocks muscles. Core stabilizers are the smaller postural muscles closer to the bones. They stabilize the skeletal system, align the body and improve breathing. They also improve coordination. The larger superficial muscles lie closer to the skin and provide power for moving the body through space. The foundation of Pilates training is to establish a strong core during EVERY movement.

Core Control Champion Exercise: This exercise uses visualization in combination with the power of dynamic Lateral Breathing to activate your Powerhouse. Building a strong core foundation is the key to Pilates and all efficient movement.

Lateral Breathing: Pilates term for your inhalations in which the rib cage inflates and expands side to side and into the back surfaces of the body. Your exhalations bring the front of the ribs together and scoop out the pelvic area. It is the key to Pilates and strength endurance training.

Navel to Spine Scoop: This is the mental image for core control to help you physically draw the abdominal muscles inward and upward. The result is a hollow or scooped appearance in the hips and waistline.

Neutral Pelvic Posture: This is the position of the spine referred to as neutral. This position provides safety for all movements. The lower back is neither arched nor curved. Neutral is the comfortable place in between these two with a slight natural arch in the lower back. Lie down on your back to find neutral. Elongate your spine and sink your navel to your spine. Flatten your lower back to the floor and then arch it away from the floor. Neutral is the comfortable place in between these two positions.

Parachute or Image for Core Control: The physical and mental act of the abdominals contracting to support the body to stand upright, move the limbs and expel air. Feel the powerful elastic action of wearing a parachute harness like while skydiving. The harness draws the abdominals upward away from your hips, in toward your spine, and finally up underneath your rib cage. Visualize drawing your abdominal wall in, back, and up. The center of your body takes on a hollow scooped-out bowl shape.

Pelvic Floor: Cough to feel the pelvic floor muscles. The Base of the Powerhouse includes these muscles. These are the bones and muscles located at the base of the pelvis.

Pilates Stance: Turn your legs out slightly. This external rotation occurs within the hip joint. The heels and legs are glued together. Squeeze your glutes (buttocks muscles) together and wrap the backs of the thighs toward each other.

Powerhouse: Powerhouse is the name Joseph Pilates gave to the abdominal area between the ribs and hips. The Powerhouse is a label used to describe the combination of muscles of your abdominals, gluteals (buttock muscles), and lower back. It is also referred to as your core muscles. Recruiting the Powerhouse BEFORE you move protects your body. Initiate and follow through every Pilates and calisthenics' movement from the center of the body or your Powerhouse.

Shoulder Blades, Scapula: The pair of triangular bones lying on either side of the upper back area. They can glide up (elevation) and down (depression), in toward the spine (retraction), away from the spine (protraction) and rotate upward and downward. Maintain proper shoulder girdle organization as you exercise by keeping the shoulder girdle from hiking up toward the ears.

Shoulder Girdle Organization: This upper body trunk structure stabilizes the upper body so the arms can move with ease.

Vine or Image for Core Control: The physical and mental act of contracting the abdominals to support the body. Visualize your abdominal muscle fibers sliding and interweaving across each other like a strong, winding vine.

Visual Imagery: The use of a mental picture to accomplish physical tasks with success and safety. Visualization is an essential element in sports, dance and Pilates. It is also extremely helpful for stress management and healing. It helps the mind through a profound inwardly directed focus to more effectively control the body.

Pilates and Calisthenics for Children

Child's Name: _____

Is hereby recognized for their knowledge of the ABCs of movement.

These Alignment, Breathing and Core Control anatomy-based mind/body visual images generate a

lifetime of fitness enjoyment and health!

Effective this _____ day of _____

Congratulations!

LARKIN BARNETT, President's Challenge Advocate

Teacher/Parent _____